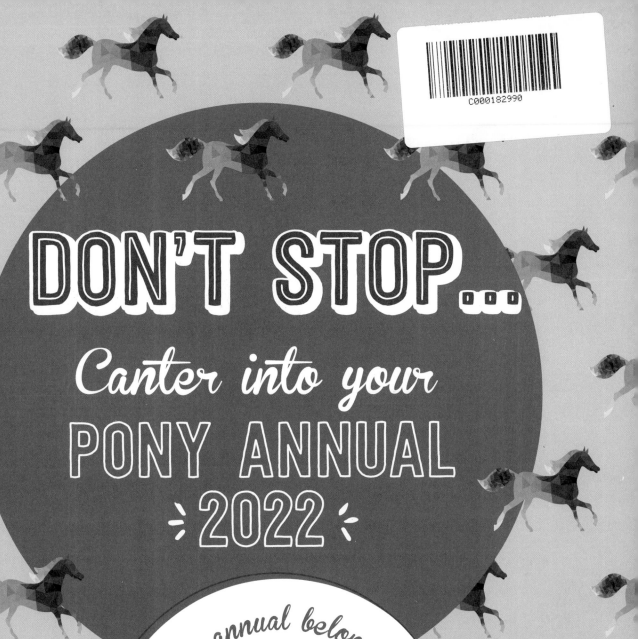

DON'T STOP...

Canter into your

PONY ANNUAL

⋙ 2022 ⋘

This annual belongs to

PONY
THE ANNUAL 2022

INSIDE

86

88

32

58

An awesome horseshoe make on p72

Published by DJ Murphy (Publishers) Ltd, Olive Studio, The Timber Yard, Grange Road, Tilford, Farnham, Surrey GU10 2DQ

Who did what in PONY – The Annual
Contributors Kiera Boyle, Sarah Burgess, Megan Hurley, Louise Kittle, Bethany Searby
Design Adam Witt, Jake Booth

PONY magazine is published every four weeks. To find out more about PONY magazine, visit ponymag.com
© Copyright DJ Murphy (Publishers) Ltd 2021

Printed by Graphicom via dell'Industria – 36100 Vicenza, Italy

ISBN 978-1-913787-05-9

MIX
Paper from responsible sources
FSC® C013123
FSC
www.fsc.org

YOUR ANNUAL

6

Make a Charlie cake on p24!

48

READY, SET GOAL!

Find out how goal setting could help make your riding dreams come true

Everyone has a goal or two they dream of achieving with their fave pony – maybe it's jumping a 70cm course or learning how to leg-yield. Even if you don't compete, it's still super-important you have goals to aim for in your riding. Plus, goal-setting is a super-useful skill in and out of the saddle. So, here are our five steps to successful goal setting to help you and your fave pony reach for the stars!

1 Your heart's desire

The first – and most important – part of setting your goal is to figure out what it is you want to achieve. That could be having a go at your first dressage test, taking your new pony on your first hack together or even qualifying for the Pony Club Championships. Make sure you stick to one or two main goals at a time to help you focus on achieving them. The fewer goals, the more time and energy you'll be able to dedicate to reaching them. Once you've picked your main goal, you can then focus on how you're going to get there.

TOP TIP
It can be super-helpful to share your goals with friends to give your confidence a boost and make your dreams feel closer to reality!

2

Small but mighty

Breaking down your main aim into small, achievable steps will help you make a plan of how to get where you want to be without it feeling overwhelming. For example, if your big goal is to compete on a Pony Club showjumping team this year, your first step could be to find out your club's requirements for being on a team – it might mean attending a certain number of rallies or proving your ability at that level as an individual. Setting a series of mini goals will make your main one feel more achievable, otherwise it might seem like it's a long way off, which can be really demotivating.

 Learning new skills and teaching your pony new things will take time

3

Time it right

Vague ideas won't be very useful when to comes to achieving your goal, so make sure you're really specific about what you want to do. Your mini goals should help you get one step closer to reaching your dream – if it's just a tiny movement in the right direction.

Another super-important part of goal-setting is giving yourself a realistic timeframe. Remember that learning new skills and teaching your pony new things will take time, so don't try to rush your mini goals. But giving yourself a deadline will help motivate you and make sure you get where you want to be. Things don't always go to plan – especially with ponies – but if you allow plenty of time and put some thought into your goals, you're sure to get there – even if it takes a little bit longer than you might have hoped.

4 Moving on up

Learning how to handle setbacks is another important part of achieving your goals. Things going wrong is part of riding – even if you do everything right – so being able to roll with the punches and keep moving forward is key to getting where you want to be. Give yourself time to feel disappointed that your session or show didn't go as planned, then make some adjustments to your mini goals if you feel you need to. This isn't a failure! Being flexible is a great quality and there's nothing wrong with changing your aims if you need more time or have changed your mind about what you want to achieve.

TOP TIP
Ask your instructor for help with your goal-setting. They'll make sure your aims are achievable and that the time you've allocated for them is realistic!

5 Take note

Include details of each ride, including what worked well

It's a great idea to keep a diary where you can write down your main and mini goals, and your deadlines for achieving them. You could even include details of each ride, including what worked well and anything you need to practise more. This will help you keep an eye on how close you're getting to your goal, as well as giving you a great opportunity to look back over all the work you've done and how you and your fave pony have progressed.

TOP TIP
Don't forget to take some time to feel proud of yourself! It's easy to focus super-hard on reaching your goals and forget how far you've come, so make sure you give yourself a pat on the back for what you've accomplished already.

Why not fill in the diary yourself? What do you want to achieve this year? **Download the page at bit.ly/ANNUAL_GOAL_SETTING**

OALS, GOALS, GOALS!

START DATE:

END DATE:

THE GOAL

THE STRATEGY

REAK IT DOWN

ACTION STEP

TO DO
- ....
- ....
- ....

ACTION STEP

TO DO
- ....
- ....
- ....

ACTION STEP

TO DO
- ....
- ....
- ....

HE REWARD:

RAD RIDE AND TIE

Get to grips with this tough sport!

R ide and tie is an incredible race involving two people and one horse. It combines running, riding, endurance and strategy. But what's it really all about? Find out here!

Back in time

The Ride and Tie Association was formed in 1988, although the sport was invented in the 1960s, with the first-ever event held on 6 June 1971 near St Helena, California. The sport was developed by Bud Johns, who worked for a company looking for a rugged sport to promote its outdoor clothing line.

Bud was a history fanatic and read historic accounts of pairs using one horse to cover huge distances. One would ride, while the other followed on foot. After a while, the horseman would leave his mount tied to a tree and the runner would have a rested horse to catch up on. And so, the sport of ride and tie was born!

Race day

The aim of the race is to get your three team members – two human and one equine – across a 20–100 mile cross-country course, alternating who rides and who runs. To begin with, the rider goes ahead, with the runner following behind. At a predetermined point the rider ties the horse to a tree or fence post and continues on foot. The runner reaches the horse, mounts and catches up his team mate.

The rider can do a flying tie, which means they swap as soon as they catch the runner, or overtake and tie up the horse again. This is where the strategy comes in, because how you swap could have a big effect on the outcome of the race. Every member will have different strengths, so each team has to think carefully about its plan beforehand.

PONY recommends you wear an up-to-standard riding hat when mounted at all times

Pre- and post-race checks include pulse, respiration rates, mucous membrane colour, capillary refill, attitude and soundness assessments.

Rulebound

Just like any comp, ride and tie has lots of rules to get your head around, including...

- equine competitors needing to be at least five years old
- pre- and post-race examinations for all horses to make sure they're fit and healthy
- nobody outside the team can handle the horse – except in the case of one escaping!
- only one team member may ride the horse at a time!
- teams have to report to trail marshals around the course to make sure they aren't taking any short-cuts

KITTED OUT

What should you have in your grooming kit? Find out here...

Knowing what to put in your grooming kit – not to mention what everything does – can be pretty tricky. Do you know a rubber curry comb from a dandy brush? Test your knowledge, and even learn something new, with our grooming kit guide.

Feet first!

A hoof pick is a grooming kit must-have. Picking out your fave pony's feet regularly is super-important for keeping his hooves healthy. It also gives you the chance to check his feet for signs of injury or damage.

TOP TIP
Check your pony's shoes when picking out his feet to make sure they still fit well and look secure.

Dream coat

Body brushes are for removing dust and dirt from your pony's coat, mane and tail. They're softer than a dandy brush and will help get your pony's coat really shiny. A dandy brush has rougher bristles and is perfect for removing lots of mud and dirt on ponies who live out – but don't use it on any sensitive or clipped areas of his body!

Head and shoulders

There are a few different types of mane and tail comb, including small metal or plastic combs, and bigger brushes that look a bit like your hairbrush. You might need a comb to keep the hair knot-free and looking really tidy.

Mud-free

Plastic and rubber curry combs are a great way to remove caked-on mud or dirt from your pony's coat. A rubber curry comb is also really handy to help remove his winter coat when he's moulting.

Brush up

Use a metal curry comb to clean your body brush while you groom to avoid putting dirt and oils back onto your pony's coat. This is especially useful when he's moulting, as the bristles on your body brush will soon end up full of hair!

TOP TIP

Why not get different-coloured sponges for each area of your pony's body so you don't get them mixed up?

Sponges

You'll need at least four sponges in your grooming kit for cleaning your fave pony's eyes, nose and dock, as well as one to wash him when he's sweaty or having a bath. Stick to sponges that don't have a green scrubbing side, as they won't be very nice for your pony!

ON COURSE FOR SUCCESS

Our step-by-step guide to preparing for the perfect clear round

Whether you're new to the showjumping world or an old hand in the ring, there's always more to learn – and new ways to score the perfect clear.

There's lots to think about on the day, but also plenty you can work on at home to give you the best possible chance of a fun and successful comp day.

1 Golden rules

Understanding the rules is an absolute must for any competition. This includes what you should wear on the day, where you register and get your number, how the collecting ring's run – there might be a limit to the number of competitors inside at any time – and whether your class is single- or two-phase. Read the schedule carefully, especially because the rules may have changed since you last competed.

TOP TIP
Single-phase classes include a timed section at the end of the course, while a two-phase class combines the first round and jump-off into one longer round.

2 Stride it out

Knowing the length of your pony's stride is super-helpful when it comes to riding related distances. If you're not sure how many of your paces equate to one of your pony's canter strides, here's an exercise to help you find out...

1. Place two poles on a straight line 3m apart.
2. Walk and trot over them on both reins to make sure your pony feels confident.
3. Approach in a bouncy jumping canter and let your pony flow over the poles.
4. If the distance between the poles felt like one perfect stride, then walk the distance between the poles on foot so you know how to count one of his strides in your paces.
5. If your pony chipped in an extra stride or stood off the second pole, move the poles closer together or further apart until you find the distance to match his stride.

Once you know how many of your paces equal one of your pony's canter strides, you'll be able to easily count and predict how many of his strides he'll fit into a related distance on course.

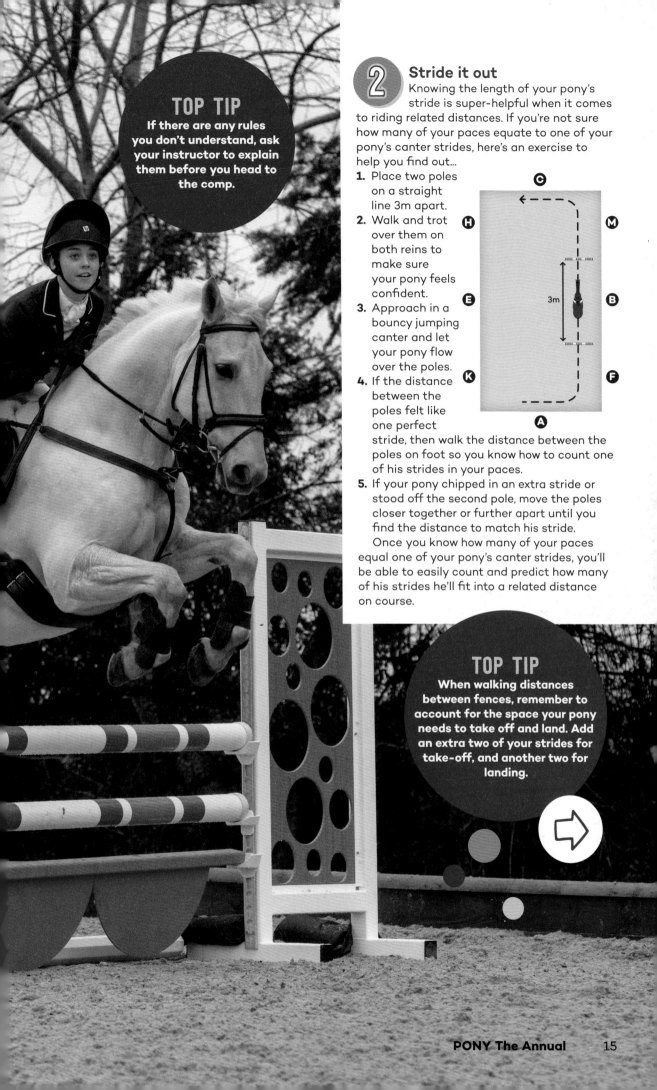

3 Spotter's guide

Knowing all the fences you might meet on course is really helpful because it means you'll be able to practise them before comp day. It might be a while before you have to tackle a triple bar or water tray in competition, but there's no harm in being able to spot them and maybe even having a go at some small ones with your instructor.

Here are some examples of what you might meet out on course...

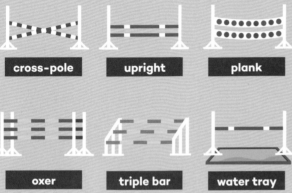

cross-pole   upright   plank

oxer   triple bar   water tray

4 Perfect paces

Being able to create a powerful and balanced canter at home is great prep for the ring. Your pony's showjumping canter should be energetic and bouncy without feeling rushed, but it should also be adjustable. Here's a quick exercise that'll put to the test...

1. In canter, ride large around the outside of the arena.
2. At the end of the long side, ride a 15m circ in the corner. Sit tall, keeping a little inside bend, and half-halt to balance your pony.
3. Use the circle to encourage your pony to engage his hindquarters.
4. Once you've finished the circle, ride large and try again after the next long side.
5. Make plenty of changes of rein to ensure he's working both sides of his body evenly.

This is really hard work if your pony isn't used to it, so use the exercise little and often to get the most benefit from it.

5

Spook-tastic

Making sure your pony's really confident over fillers is important comp day prep. Practise over all sorts of obstacles to build his confidence – and help you know that there's nothing to worry about on the day! If you don't have access to fillers at your yard, there's no reason you can't still practise spooky fences. Use tyres, hay bales and arena markers to make your fences look a bit different and test your pony's bravery, but remember to secure them safely.

TOP TIP

Practise your day warm-up at home to find out what works best for your pony. That way you'll feel really prepared on the day!

6

Walk this way

Walking the course is one of the most important parts of show day, second only to your round itself! It's not just about learning what order to jump the fences in, either.

You'll need to consider what rein you want to start on (if you have a choice, try to begin on your pony's stronger rein), where you'll make jump-off turns to save time and how many strides your pony will fit into any doubles or related distances. Being really well-prepared before you jump your round will make you feel really confident and give you the best chance of going clear.

7

Wicked warm-up

Getting ready for your round is your chance to make sure your pony's jumping confidently and paying close attention to what you're asking him. He'll need to listen when you ask him to turn, slow down or go forward in the ring, so test your aids before you get on course.

Practise transitions and make loads of shapes and changes of rein before you start jumping. Then, build up your warm-up fences gradually to the height you'll be jumping in the ring. Practise jumping on an angle if you plan to take any jump-off lines. Remember to smile (it's sure to help you relax) and enjoy your round. It's all about having fun, after all!

GAME ON

Nia has to prove her skills when her fave horsey game moves to the next level

Nia raced through the front door, chucked her coat and school bag on the floor and rushed upstairs to her bedroom. She ignored her mum telling her to come back and pick up the mess and popped on her headphones. She'd been waiting all day to get back online so she could play her all-time favourite game, *Rosewood Ranch*.

The magic happens
Nia loved playing as her character Esmerelda Saddlebottom. She had an awesome competition record and a stunning horse –Cobalt – who she'd designed. Cobalt was her dream horse – black with a stripe and four perfect white socks.

As Nia trekked through the virtual forest, she was interrupted by her mum calling from downstairs. "You're always on that game, Nia. Why don't you get some fresh air and play outside?"

"Maybe later!" Nia yelled back. She returned to her game and sighed. *I wish my life was as exciting as Esmerelda's...*

Then she felt her computer and desk start to shake. Confused, she stared at her screen and saw the words 'Welcome to *Rosewood Ranch*' appear in huge letters. Nia wanted to scream but, in a flash, she vanished.

> **What if winning the comp's my only ticket back home?**

Unknown territory
With a thud, Nia landed face first on a dirt path. "Ugh!" she cried. Standing up, she looked around, dazed. *Where am I? It feels like I'm in some kind of forest.* Nia brushed herself off to get rid of the dirt, but realised her body felt different. She was taller and wearing the most gorgeous outfit ever. Wandering over to a puddle, she peered down at her reflection and gasped – Esmerelda Saddlebottom was looking back up at her! Suddenly, Nia heard a snort come from behind her. She turned and was faced with a mighty black stallion. "Cobalt..." she breathed. Cobalt gave a shrill neigh in response. Nia certainly wasn't in her bedroom anymore.

She placed her hand on Cobalt's beautiful white stripe. He felt like a real horse, but still looked a little pixelated, like on screen. Feeling excited but a bit scared, Nia put her foot in Cobalt's stirrup and hopped into the saddle. She'd never ridden a real horse before, but she just had to think and Cobalt responded. Nia

soon found herself cantering through the forest with the wind flowing through Cobalt's long mane. He seemed to know exactly where he was taking her.

Dream ranch
Soon, Nia and Cobalt arrived at a beautiful ranch. She instantly recognised it as she'd built it all herself. Nia dismounted and headed into the barn. It took her breath away as it was exactly how she'd imagined. She looked up in awe at all of Esmerelda's rosettes pinned to a bulletin board, then heard a humming come from inside one of the stables. Nia wandered over to check it out and found Joe, the stable lad, mucking out.

"Hi there," she said. Joe stopped and turned to face her. He smiled, then began to recite a pre-recorded script: "Esmerelda, the day of the Rosewood Cup is almost here. You must reign supreme or risk losing everything. Make sure you fit in as much practise as you can."

I've never heard of the Rosewood Cup before. "What are you talking about?" Nia asked. But Joe simply began reciting the same script. He wouldn't be any more help. Nia loved being in this horsey dreamland, but she was starting to feel a little bit lonely with no one *real* to talk to. *What if losing the competition means I get trapped here for ever?*

Rising to the challenge
Luckily, Nia had spent so many hours playing *Rosewood Ranch* that she knew the game inside out. All she had to do was get Cobalt to the right level of agility, endurance and speed so she could win. She jumped onto his back and headed over to the showjumping arena. There was a glowing bubble with a horseshoe symbol in the gateway. Nia reached out and tapped it with her finger.

In a flash, they magically found themselves at an Olympic-size showjumping course. As it was only a practise run, Nia familiarised herself with the controls. She was a wiz at it normally, but things were a bit different now she was actually living as a player! Cobalt soared over the huge fences with ease, and Nia momentarily forgot that she was inside a game at all. The wind whistled past her and time seemed to stand still. How had she never ridden a horse before? It was awesome!

e main event

trained and trained until Cobalt's skill levels had
eased enough that a new bubble appeared in front
hem. It was golden, like a medal, and shimmered
the word 'Enter' in the middle. Sure enough,
tapped it and they were transported to a grand
dium with a huge crowd.

he Rosewood Cup had three phases: dressage,
ss-country and showjumping. Nia would have to
them all if she wanted to be in with a chance of
ning. First up came the dressage. Cobalt was on
form and performed the moves exactly on cue. All
had to do was squeeze him with her legs and steer
to follow the dotted path in front of her. When
y made their final salute to the judges, Nia saw
t they were in second place on the leader board.
y'd have to go clear jumping or she could risk being
ck in the game forever. As much as she was having
, she was starting to miss her family.

ail-biting finish

alt and Nia sailed through the cross-country
se as speed was his best skill. The player in the
d, Tallulah Horseman, and her pony – Lancelot –
e watching from the sidelines. *I wonder if she's a
person who's been sucked into the game, too?*
inally came the showjumping phase and it was
o play for. Nia and Cobalt watched Tallulah
l Lancelot ride their round with bated breath.
believably, Lancelot misjudged one of the fences
l knocked a pole. Now the Cup was up for grabs and
Nia had to do was get a clear round.
Nervously, the pair entered the arena for the final
e. The bell sounded and they were off. Cobalt was
ling a little tired, but Nia was determined to ride
he best of her ability. She pushed him on, meeting

each fence perfectly. With one more to go,
she squeezed Cobalt with her legs and, sure
enough, they flew over. The crowd cheered and
the commentator announced that Esmerelda and
Cobalt were the winners. Nia gave him big hug as
they were presented with the winner's sash and a huge
trophy that had the words 'Rosewood Cup Champion'
engraved onto it. As Nia stared at the shiny gold cup,
she felt her body start to tingle. A whirlwind enveloped
her and she closed her eyes. Her work here was done.

Back to reality

As suddenly as she'd departed, Nia was plonked back
onto her desk chair. She patted down her arms and
legs and was relieved to be back in her own body. She
glanced round her familiar bedroom. *How long have I
been gone?* As she turned back to her screen, she saw
Cobalt in his stable – his winner's sash hanging across
the door. Nia felt a pang of sadness that she could no
longer reach out and touch him.

"Nia?" her mum said as she opened the door,
offering her a mug of hot chocolate "Mum!" Nia gave
her a big hug. "Gosh, what's this for?" she replied.

"Hey, Mum, I was wondering if maybe I could start
having horse riding lessons?" Nia's mum looked quite
shocked. "Really? Normally you hate anything that
involves going outdoors."

"I know," Nia replied. "But I think you're right. There's
more to life than just living through a screen. I want
to ride a pony for real." Nia's mum smiled. "That's
great to hear! I'll ring up the local riding school in the
morning and see if I can book you in." Nia felt a glow
of happiness bubble up inside her. She may not be
competing in championships like Esmerelda but, if she
worked at it, who knew? Maybe one day she could own
a horse like Cobalt in real life!

READY FOR MY CLOSE-UP

Can you guess these zoomed-in pony care tools?

CHECK OUT P100 FOR THE ANSWERS

I SCORED /12

1. S _ _ _ _ _ _ _ _
_ _ _ _

2. B _ _ _ _ _ _

3. S _ _ _ _ _ _

4. H _ _ _ _ _ _ _

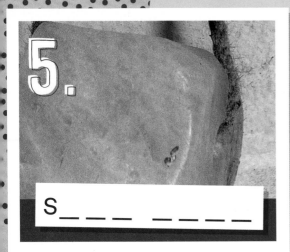

5.

S_ _ _ _   _ _ _ _ _

6.

G_ _ _ _ _   _ _ _ _ _ _

7.

S_ _ _ _ _ _ _ _

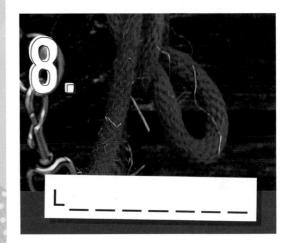

8.

L_ _ _ _ _ _ _ _

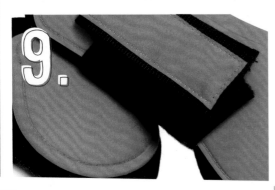

9.

T_ _ _ _ _ _   _ _ _ _ _

10.

D_ _ _ _ _   _ _ _ _ _ _

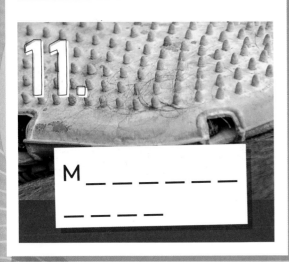

11.

M_ _ _ _ _ _ _

_ _ _ _ _

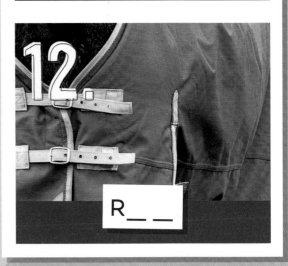

12.

R_ _ _

SUPER SKIJOR

Have you ever heard of this spectacular sport?

A crazy blend of sledding and driving, skijor is a mega mix that's as exciting as it is unusual. If you love the idea of combining skiing with ponies, you've come to the right place!

Comp ready

Equine skijoring requires a team of one horse and two people, one of whom rides while the other skis holding a rope attached to the horse – a bit like water skiing! The horses gallop down a 270–370m track and the skier navigates a range of jumps and gates – sometimes they even have to grab rings as they go! The horse usually gallops in a straight line with the skier negotiating obstacles either side of them, but some races are run on a horseshoe-shaped track that allows the skier to stay to the outside.

Many competitors use modified water skiing equipment, while others attach a tow rope to the saddle horn of a western saddle, or hook up two towing lines to the back of the saddle or a breastplate.

Time machine

Harnessing reindeer and being pulled along on skis has been used as a method of transport in Scandanavia for hundreds of years and, by 1912, skijoring behind horses was popular in Switzerland and France.

Around the same time, equine skijoring made the trip across the Atlantic to the USA. By the 1930s, towns in Colorado and Wyoming were holding held equine skijoring races in the streets.

The sport made its official debut at the Winter Games in Stockholm in 1901, returning in 1906 and 1909. Equine skijoring featured in the 1928 Winter Olympic Games in Switzerland. While it's not appeared since, there are hopes to bring it back to the 2026 Olympics. Just like snow polo, the sport gets its most exposure at White Turf in St Moritz, Switzerland.

DID YOU KNOW?

Some events run novelty classes, such as the longest jump with a flat landing – some competitors have reached 17m!

Where in the world?

There are lots of venues for competitive skijoring all over the world, including...

- Switzerland
- France
- Denmark
- Latvia
- Sweden
- Russia
- Ukraine
- Finland
- Norway
- the USA

CHARLIE CAKE

Make your very own cake of PONY mascot, Charlie!

YOU'LL NEED

FOR THE CAKE

- ✓ 175g butter, softened
- ✓ 175g caster sugar
- ✓ 3 medium eggs, beaten
- ✓ 1 tsp vanilla extract
- ✓ 175g self-raising flour
- ✓ 1 tsp baking powder
- ✓ 4 tbsp strawberry jam
- ✓ Brown sugar paste
- ✓ Black sugar paste
- ✓ White sugar paste
- ✓ Red sugar paste

FOR THE BUTTERCREAM

- ✓ 175g butter, softened
- ✓ 375g icing sugar, plus extra for dusting
- ✓ 1½ tsp vanilla extract
- ✓ 6 tsp milk

1. Heat the oven to 180°C or 160°C for a fan oven. Grease two 20cm round sandwich tins and line with baking paper. Put the butter, caster sugar, eggs and vanilla in a bowl. Sift over the flour and baking powder. Beat the mixture with a whisk or electric mixer until thick.

2. Divide the mixture evenly between the tins, levelling the tops with the back of a spoon. Bake for 25–30 mins, or until firm to the touch. Leave to cool for a few minutes, then turn out onto a wire rack to cool fully.

3. To make the buttercream, place the butter, icing sugar, vanilla extract and milk into a mixing bowl. Beat together with a wooden spoon until smooth and fluffy.

rim the tops of the cakes
hey're level. Place one on a
e board and spread over the
wberry jam followed by a third
e buttercream. Place the
r cake on top.

5. Using a sharp knife, cut the two sides of the cake into an oval. You can make a template for the shape out of paper.

6. Using a palette knife, cover the top and sides with the rest of the buttercream and smooth the surface, then set aside.

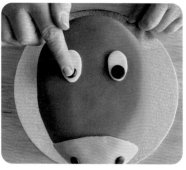

ust your worksurface lightly
icing sugar. Roll out the
vn sugar paste and cover
cake. Smooth the paste
your hands,
trim the
ss with
arp
e.

TOP TIP
You can change the colours of the sugar paste to make the cake look like your pony!

I. Mix some of the brown sugar paste with white sugar paste to get a paler colour. Using a small rolling pin, roll it out and cut out a small oval. Place it on the cake where Charlie's muzzle would be. Use a little brush to paint a small amount of water on the underside of the muzzle so it sticks. Mould two nostrils with black sugar paste and stick on the muzzle with a little water.

2. Make two balls of white sugar paste and squash them between your fingers to make ovals for the eyes, then add black balls of sugar paste to make the eyeballs. Add a small white dot. Like with the muzzle, use a small amount of water on a paint brush to attach them. Add eye lashes in the same way.

ix a little white and red sugar
te to make it pink. Shape ears
n the brown paste, add a pink
re and place on either side at
top of Charlie's head.

4. Create the headcollar by rolling two sausages of red sugar paste. Stick them on the pony's head and flatten them gently with your fingers.

5. Roll sausage shapes of black sugar paste and layer them where his forelock would be.

FINISHED!

FRIENDLY FACES

PART ONE

Making friends on a new yard isn't always easy

Ruby and Dilly as
Amy and **Sunny**

Lily and Penny as
Helena and **Pickle**

Hollie and Moon as
Ellie and **Blue**

Find out how Sunny found her first few days at the new yard on p74!

Little 'n' Large

SHETLANDS
AND SHIRES

Learn all about these awesome breeds!

Super Shetlands

Shetland ponies are known for being super-cute, but that's not all they get up to! The Shetland pony's ancestors have lived on the Shetland Isles since the Bronze Age – around 5,000 years ago! Their hardy and tough nature meant they were perfect for pulling carts, ploughing and carrying coal.

During the Industrial Revolution in the 19th Century, thousands of Shetland ponies were transported to the mainland where they were used as pit ponies, hauling coal out of mines. This is a long way from their jobs today, which include being children's ponies, carriage driving and even therapeutic work.

FACT FILE

Home country: Shetland Isles, Scotland
Height: Up to 107cm
Colours: Black, dark brown, bay or chestnut
Uses: Riding, driving and as pack pony

Stunning Shires

hires are well-known for being brilliant draught horses, lling ploughs, canal boats and even brewers' drays. The glish Cart Horse Society was formed in 1878, holding its st ever Spring Show in London with 117 heavy horses on splay! In 1884 the society was renamed the Shire Horse ciety, and began to develop educational activities to prove the treatment and care of working horses . Once machines became widespread for farming and ansport, draught horses weren't needed. By the 1960s eir numbers had fallen to a couple of thousand, and the eed is considered at risk by the Rare Breeds Survival Trust. wever, it seems to be enjoying a bit of a comeback – me smaller farms are using Shires rather than machines d they're still used for forestry work. Ploughing matches d agricultural shows also feature plenty of Shires, too.

FACT FILE

Home country: Cambridgeshire and Lincolnshire, England
Height: 16–18hh
Colours: Black, bay, roan or grey
Uses: Driving and draught work

HAPPY HACKING

Top tips to remember while exploring the great outdoors

Taking your pony out hacking is an awesome way to explore the countryside. There are tonnes of different places you can go. We've got loads of awesome tips to help you stay safe while you're out and about, so can have the most fun ever!

Be safe, be seen

Whenever you go hacking, it's vital that you and your pony wear hi-viz clothing. This way, you'll stand out to other road users, giving drivers more time to slow down when they see you. You still need to wear hi-viz on bridleways and in fields, too. This is because it makes it easier for walkers, other riders or off-road vehicles to spot you.

TOP TIP

Always thank drivers by raising your hand nodding and smiling when they drive past slowly.

DID YOU KNOW?

When you wear hi-viz out hacking, drivers will see you three seconds earlier than if you aren't. That's loads more time for them to slow down!

Rules of the road

Before you head off your yard, it's important to be familiar with the rules of the road. You can learn all about them by reading the Highway Code, and be sure to pay close attention to the section related to horses. It's also a great idea to work towards your Pony Club Road Rider test or BHS Ride Safe award. To get you started, some key things to remember when you're riding on the road are...

- keep to the left
- always look and signal before making a turn
- keep both feet in the stirrups and both hands on the reins, unless you're signalling
- wear hi-viz
- never ride more than two abreast, and stay in single file around bends and on narrow lanes

Good signs

When you're hacking, you'll likely come across some different road signs. They're designed to help keep road users safe, so it's vital to understand what they mean. Here are few common ones you might see...

Stop

Traffic lights ahead

Give way

Roundabout

Two way traffic

Farm traffic

Pace yourself

You can ride in a variety of paces while you're out on a hack, but stick to walk while you're on the road and save trot and canter for suitable fields and bridleways.

Walking on roads is an awesome way to harden your pony's tendons so they get super-strong, and it's brill for his fitness, too. Trotting on roads can be fun, but only do it in short intervals and on uphill stretches, because the jarring can be hard on your pony's legs.

Got the spooks

Hacking's a fab way to expose your pony to new things so he can become super-brave and confident. However, he needs to learn to react safely to something that looks scary. When he pricks his ears at a spooky garden waste bag or pushchair, let him have a little look, then squeeze him on with your legs. If you turn your head away from the scary object and stay calm, it'll indicate to him that there's nothing to be afraid of!

TOP TIP

If your pony's prone to being a bit spooky on hacks, why not bring a friend with you? That way, if you meet something he doesn't like, your friend's pony can help lead him past and build up his bravery.

The right path

When you're navigating the countryside, you're sure to come across a few different types of off-road track. Be careful, because ponies aren't allowed on all of them. So, make sure you know where you can and can't go before heading out.

TYPE	WHO USES IT?	PONY FRIENDLY?
Footpath	Pedestrians	✗
Cycle path	Pedestrians and cyclists	✗
Bridleway	Pedestrians, cyclists and horse riders	✓
Restricted byway	Pedestrians, cyclists, horse riders and non-motorised vehicles	✓
Byway	Pedestrians, cyclists, horse riders and motorised vehicles	✓

Make a splash

You may encounter a stream, ford or river while you're out riding. Most ponies enjoy going into the water to have a splash about, and walking and trotting through it can add resistance to help build muscle. It's also great practise for water jumps when you go cross-country, and to cool your pony down in warm weather!

But, before you take him for a paddle, you need to make sure it's safe to do so. Stick to shallow water, and check that the riverbed and banks aren't too soft and squelchy, because your pony could get stuck.

Ford

Soft verges

Get up and go!

Once you're clued up on all the rules and signs on the road, you're ready to get out hacking! It's so much fun to explore the world on horseback that, as long as you stay safe, it's sure to become your fave thing ever!

RONNIE THE RESCUE PONY

The life of a pony isn't always smoothly paved, especially if he's a rescue...

You might look at me and think now *there's* a pony who's got it all. Glossy coat, cosy stable and a humongous field to frolic in – what more could a Welsh Mountain want? Well, not so long ago, my life wasn't the fairytale it is today. If you saw the scrapes I got into you'd say "Ronnie, how on *earth* did you get out of that one?" While I'd like to give my wits all the credit, I had a lot of help from some very special people along the way.

Humble beginnings

My journey began at a Welsh pony stud nestled in a lush valley. It was a pony paradise and I spent my days running about with the other foals while our mums watched over us. When I was old enough to be ridden, I was taught to be a super show pony with perfect manners.

Then the day came that I'd have to leave the stud for a new life – something my mum had prepared me for. Along came a family who had a little girl. She picked me out and asked boldly if she could take me for a ride. She didn't have much balance and bopped around a lot in the saddle, but I made sure to be extra careful, just like I'd been taught. She was kicking my sides quite a lot and I wasn't sure why, but I didn't react. When it was time for her to get off I was a little relieved, but the girl seemed overjoyed. Sure enough, not long after, the family returned towing a trailer behind their car to take me home with them.

My new home

The first months in my new home weren't anything like what I was used at the stud. The girl spent time grooming me initially and we had a few rides around the field in walk, but she was nowhere near as experienced as the stud grooms and didn't always give me what I needed. I only had very small haynets, my field was covered in poo and flies and sometimes I was thirsty, but my water bucket was left empty for days at a time.

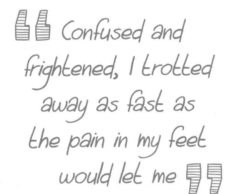

Confused and frightened, I trotted away as fast as the pain in my feet would let me

When winter came, things got even worse. The gi[rl] stopped coming to visit all together, so her dad wou[ld] come instead. He never stayed for long and always seemed grumpy, only ever throwing me a bit of hay over the stable door. I wasn't turned out in the field anymore – I was stuck in my tiny stable, with my be[d] getting muckier and muckier. Occasionally the dad would pick up some of the poo, but the smell wasn't very pleasant. My feet grew long and hurt where I w[as] standing in wet bedding all the time. As time went [on] I felt more and more down, and hu[ng] my head most days, wondering w[hat] I'd done to deserve such a sad life.

A turn for the worse

Late one night, I heard a car pull u[p] outside the stable. I thought it wa[s a] strange time for anyone to visit, b[ut] I didn't have the energy to raise m[y] head to look. It was the girl's dad, [and] he roughly put a headcollar on me[,] forcing me out of the stable. I had[n't] walked properly in so long that I limped as he dragged me, my hoo[ves] really hurting and limbs aching. H[e] pulled on my headcollar impatiently while muttering something about 'losing a job'. I couldn't work out what was the matter and felt very nervous. He led me into the same trailer he'd picked me up in. Was I finally going back to my old home? Feeling a flicker of hopefulness, I walked up the ramp obediently an[d] stood patiently as we drove off into the night.

After a while, we stopped. I stepped gingerly off the trailer into darkness, not knowing where I was. Before I knew it, the dad smacked my bottom with [a] huge lunge whip and shouted at me. Confused and frightened, I trotted away as fast as the pain in my feet would let me. It soon began to rain and I got ve[ry] cold and shivery. My feet hurt so much that I had to [lie] down under a tree. What was I going to do now?

A friendly face

For several days, I wondered aimlessly around the forest. I managed to find a little bit of grass to nibb[le] on, but my face was getting sore from the tight headcollar I still had on. I accidently walked across

e barbed wire and got a bad gash on my leg.
s exhausted and losing hope by the second.
ne day, I was resting my injured leg under
nopy of trees when I noticed a woman
roaching me. I flinched, but didn't have the
ngth to run way. I blinked my eyes and saw
had a kind face and an apple slice in her
d. I decided to trust her – it wasn't like I had
y other options – and gently took the treat
e she clipped a leadrope onto my headcollar.
walked me slowly to a nearby farmyard
re she threw a blanket over me and popped
nto a stable with a deep straw bed. I had a
of hay that was nearly as tall as me.
ater that day, the kind-faced woman
rned and led me out of the stable. I saw
a horsebox was waiting to take me
ewhere. Now where was I off to?

afe haven

arrived at a place with more horses and ponies
I'd ever seen before. I was put in a stable while
wounds and feet were treated – oh, it felt so much
er! Once I'd regained my strength, I was allowed
a field with a few other ponies, who told me I'd
brought here to be looked after and to have a
home found for me. The place reminded me of the
I grew up on and I felt like I might have caught a
ke of luck.

here were lots of humans at this not-stud, and
all made a big fuss of me. Before I knew it, I felt
uch healthier and my feet didn't hurt any more.
y discovered that I was a fabulous riding pony with
eccable manners, and soon started talking about
ing me a new home. I was devastated. I liked the
-stud – what if they sent me to a family who'd
ect me again?

end or foe?

rtly after that, an unfamiliar car pulled up at the
stud. A family with not one, but *two*, little girls
out and there was an air of excitement among my
y friends. "This could be it, Ronnie," one of them
me. "Go to the gate and greet them!" Not likely,
ught, and turned my back. I didn't want to be
ked away again. As luck wouldn't have it, one of

the little girls spotted me and wanted to say hello.
I tried to remain aloof, but it was hard when they
looked up at me with expectant faces. Gentleman
that I am, I let them brush and fuss over me – secretly
enjoying the cuddles I'd been missing.

My tack was brought out and it was clear the
girls wanted to ride. Now, I'm not proud of it, but I
considered being naughty to keep my place at the
not-stud. In the end, I just couldn't bring myself to
do it and I trotted around the school on my best
behaviour. It reminded me how good it felt to be a
child's show pony, and I couldn't help but flaunt my
floaty paces. But was I ready to go to *another* new
home?

A fresh start

The girls and their parents came back a few times to
see me, and would always hurry over to make a fuss of
me. I started to look forward to seeing them more and
more, and dreaded them leaving. One day, they led me
out of the yard and straight into a horsebox – I was
officially going home with them!

Since that day, life has never been better. I live right
outside my new humans' house with their other horses,
and spend hours with the little girls every day. I'm so
grateful that, though I was shy and surly, my family
saw their perfect pony in me. I'm now living the life of
Riley, or should that be the life of Ronnie?

A PONY STRING ARTWORK

Make a gorgeous piece of art to hang on your bedroom wall

YOU'LL NEED

✓ Wooden board
✓ Nails
✓ Hammer
✓ Thread
✓ Template
✓ Paint and brush

TOP TIP

What's your yard bestie's fave colour? String art's a great birthday gift!

Turn to p101 for the template

...ep your wooden ...rd by painting in ...r chosen colour.

Ask an adult for help when using a hammer.

2. Use nails to pin down the template onto the board. Make sure you leave a centimetre border.

3. Begin to work your way around the dotted lines, putting nails at even intervals.

...Once all the nails ...in, it should look ...ilar to this!

5. Now tear the template off the board.

TOP TIP
Make sure you tear slowly so the nails stay in place!

6. Grab your chosen thread and tie it to a corner nail.

...ow begin wrapping the ...ad between the nails. ...efully follow the template to ...e the horse in silhouette.

8. Using more thread and different angles will add extra colour and make your artwork really stand out!

WOW!
When you're finished, display your artwork for all to see!

PONY EVOLUTION

Learn all about how ponies have developed over time

Ponies have been around for millions of years, but they haven't always looked the way they do now. They've evolved over time to become the modern horses we know today. We've got loads of info on what they were like in the past, and how they've developed.

Eohippus

JOURNEY THROUGH TIME
Ponies have changed a lot over the years. Take a trip through history and discover their history...

55 MILLION YEARS AGO

32-20 MILLION YEARS AGO

20-15 MILLION YEARS AGO

Eohippus
The name Eohippus is a Greek word that means 'dawn horse'. Identified as the first ancestor of the modern horse, its remains have been discovered in North America.

Standing at around 8hh, Eohippus had four toes on its front feet and three on its back, with longer hindlegs than front legs so it could outrun predators.

Mesohippus
Meaning 'middle horse', Mesohippus was larger than Eohippus. With only three toes on each foot, it was a grazing animal like modern horses, but its teeth weren't as advanced as the horses we know today. It had six cheek teeth and a seventh small one, which is the origin of wolf teeth that some horses still have today.

Merychippus
Standing around 10hh, Merychippus had lots more features we'd recognise in modern horses. For example, its eyes were wider apart and set further back so it could see all around, and it had a bigger brain too! Merychippus had longer, more slender legs and was the first ancestor with a long neck and head, too.

Horses originated in North America, but were believed to have become extinct there during the Ice Age. Until recently, it was thought that horses were reintroduced to America by the Spanish settlers in the 1500s. However, recent evidence shows that some equines did survive there, and were ridden by Native Americans long before the continent was discovered by Spanish explorers.

DID YOU KNOW?

Tapirs and rhinoceroses are the closest living relatives to equines.

15 MILLION YEARS AGO

TODAY

Pliohippus

Known as the grandfather of the modern horse, Pliohippus was one of three different species of Equus at the time – but it's believed to be the most closely related to modern horses. It had one toe on each foot and its teeth were longer so it could graze more easily.

Equus

Around 2.5 million years ago, a land bridge connected North America to Europe. Some of the Equus species migrated to Europe, Asia and Africa across this bridge, where they evolved into the horses, donkeys and zebras we know today. Over the last few thousand years, humans have had a big impact on the shape and size of the horses we know today to help them become the perfect riding horse.

SPOT THE SIGNS

Ponies still have some tell-tale signs you might be able to spot that are leftover from their ancestors.

Brain power

Have you ever heard the joke: a horse walks into a bar and the barman asks why the long face? Well, the answer may just be because ponies' heads have evolved to allow more space for their brain! As well as growing bigger on the outside, ponies' brains have evolved over time, too. A modern horse's brain is around the size of a grapefruit, but Eohippus' head was much smaller, which tells us its brain was smaller, too.

DID YOU KNOW?

Ever wonder if your pony's smarter than you? Well, a modern horse's brain is said to be the same size as a human child's!

Long in the tooth

Ponies' teeth have changed a lot over time. This is mainly due to their changing environment. Over time, equids went from eating fruit and leaves in tropical rainforests to grazing grassland in open prairies. This shift influenced a lot of things about ponies' bodies, but his teeth are a big part. They've grown longer and sharper to graze easily. If you look at your pony's teeth, you'll be able to see how long they are – millions of years ago, his teeth would've been much smaller and there wouldn't have been so many of them.

Back on track

Now ideal for ridden work, horses' backs have evolved to be stronger and straighter. Eohippus had a very short, arched back which looked totally different to what we'd recognise today. This means it would have moved very differently, too, and wouldn't have been anywhere near as fast or had as much stamina as modern horses.

" Horses used to have toes rather than hooves! "

Hoof it

Horses used to have toes rather than hooves! The middle toe gradually evolved into a single hoof, and the outer ones lost their purpose. Having long legs and hooves helps horses run faster to escape predators in open areas where there's nowhere to hide. You can still see little indicators on your pony's body where his toes used to be! These are...

Ergots A little nail some ponies have on the underside of their fetlock. Some have two while others have none. They're thought to be leftover from when horses had toes.

Chestnuts A callus found on the inside of a pony's leg, around knee-height. Some ponies have one on each leg, but others only have them on their front legs.

DID YOU KNOW?

Chestnuts were sometimes called night eyes. This is because people used to think that a pony's chestnuts were the reason he could see in the dark!

Chestnut

WHAT DOES HE SEE?

Ever wondered why your pony spooks at things that just aren't scary? Let's find out

We've all been chilling out on a fun hack with our pony when, suddenly, he's taken a disliking to a wheelie bin or pheasant pottering about on the other side of a hedge.

It can be super-frustrating, but have you ever wondered why he spooks at objects he's seen lots of times before? Let's get to the bottom of some common things you'll meet on a hack that could give your pony a fright.

TOP TIP
Always ride positively and talk to your pony to encourage him when he's worried about something, as this will give him lots of confidence to get past it.

DID YOU KNOW?
Some ponies are naturally spookier than others, so don't be disheartened if your pony's frightened by things your friend's isn't – they're all different!

SIGNS OF A SPOOK

Spooks can sometimes feel like they've come out of nowhere! But there are a couple of subtle signs that might help you spot when one's inbound. Your pony might...

- lift his head up high
- prick his ears
- slow down or stop
- tense his body
- blow out through his nostrils

Ponies are flight animals, so they spook to try and keep themselves safe. If he thinks he's in danger, he's more likely to run away than face up to whatever's worrying him.

DID YOU KNOW?

Your pony's eyes are on the side of his head, which means he can see almost 360° around him. That's why he knows things are behind you before you do!

IN AND GONE

...ots of ponies take a disliking to bins of all ...apes and sizes, so yours certainly isn't ...one. Bins can look really out of place in ...eir environment, so your pony might be ...sure of them – they're tall, too, which ...n make them extra-threatening. Even ...he's encountered the same bin before, ...can look different depending on where ...u approach it from and it's likely to be ...a slightly different place each time you ...counter it.

Ride it Being able to bend your pony away from distractions is a really useful skill. It's the perfect solution for avoiding bins, but it's applicable in lots of spooky situations. Leave as much room as possible between you and the bin, then turn your shoulders and use your inside rein to bend your pony away from it. He should keep travelling forwards, but won't be looking at the bin, which makes it harder for him to spook at it!

What your pony sees

DRIVING RANGE

Cars are a common spook hazard – they're fast, noisy and often unexpected. They even look imposing when they aren't moving. Most drivers try their best to slow down and leave plenty of room when they meet a pony on the roads, but sometimes even the bravest of equines can be worried by the sound and speed of a passing car.

Ride it Practise riding near vehicles in the car park at your yard to start with, this'll get your pony used to their size and shape. Then, ride out with a friend whose pony is confident in traffic. Let them take the lead or even ride between them and the edge of the road so that your pony feels safe. Gradually take the lead when you are comfortable. Don't rush, otherwise you could risk him getting a fright.

TOP TIP
Stick to quiet times of day when getting your pony used to traffic so there aren't quite as many cars to contend with.

What your pony sees

PAW PATROL

There's no doubt we love dogs, but meeting one on a hack can be a bit scary. Owners are usually really good at putting their dogs on the lead and giving you room to pass, but a loose dog that's running around or, worse, barking, can be super-scary for your pony, especially if he's not used to them. A dog that's rushing about will trigger a pony's flight instinct, which encourages him to get away from a potential predator – you know the dog won't try to eat him, but he doesn't!

Ride it Find a friend or fellow livery with a friendly dog to introduce your pony to. Lead your pony around the yard near the dog, letting him look but regaining his attention by talking to him or asking him to turn or stop. This will help him learn that dogs aren't a big deal. Move on to riding in the field with a dog nearby, making sure you keep your pony focused on you with transitions and changes of rein.

What your pony sees

BIRDS OF A FEATHER

It's a sworn enemy of ponies everywhere – pheasants! Often found lurking in the bushes and keen to make lots of noise when they're surprised, pheasants can prove a real hassle out on a hack. Sometimes their rustling in the hedgeline is enough to spook a pony but, if not, taking off at speed and making a racket certainly will!

Ride it There's not a lot you can do about a pheasant flying out of the hedge! But riding in a relaxed, positive way will help give your pony lots of confidence. Keep your leg on and a light contact on the reins to channel his energy forwards into your hands without him feeling restricted. If there's a bird in the hedge that might take off, bend him away from it and keep riding forwards.

What your pony sees

TOP TIP

Watch out your pony doesn't try to roll when you walk through the puddle! Don't let him stop until you get out the other side.

What your pony sees

SPLISH SPLASH

Because your pony's eyes are on the side of his head, his depth perception is really poor – so while you can see to the bottom of the puddle and know exactly how deep it is, your pony can't. This can make even tiny, shallow puddles seem really scary, because he can't be sure it's not deeper than he is tall!

Ride it When you're teaching your pony to go through water, it's helpful to find bigger puddles because they're a more obvious obstacle. It's easy for him to step round smaller ones. Ride in a positive walk and look up, letting him look down at the water if he wants to. Keep nudging him forwards with your legs and voice until he steps in – you could always ask a friend to give you a lead, too.

Little 'n' Large

FALABELLAS AND BELGIAN DRAFTS

Get to know these unusual breeds!

Fantastic Falabellas

Falabellas were bred in Argentina from local horses around 1868 thanks to Patrick Newtall's breeding programme. When he died, his son-in-law, Juan Falabella – where the breed's name came from – took over. He added Welsh, Shetland and Thoroughbred bloodlines to create a herd of tiny horses.

It's all history

A formal breed registry was made in the 1940s, which aimed to standardise the breed's height. While they might be tiny, they're well-proportioned and their conformation is a lot like that of Arabs and Thoroughbreds. However, their pony ancestors gave them a thicker coat and stouter neck, plus a sturdier body.

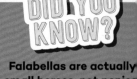

DID YOU KNOW?

Falabellas are actually small horses, not ponies despite their height.

FACT FILE

Home country: Argentina, South America
Height: 63–86cm or 25–34 inches
Colours: Bay, black, pinto, palomino or spotted
Uses: Riding, driving or showing

DID YOU KNOW?

To be registered as a pure Falabella, the horse has to be DNA tested to prove that his pedigree dates back to Juan Falabella's horses!

Brilliant Belgian Drafts

One of the strongest heavy breeds, Belgian Drafts are still used as working horses, but they're equally popular as show and riding horses. Their talent as draught horses is second to none, with a team of two pulling 7,700kg a distance of 2.18m at the National Western Stock Show in Denver, Colorado – the horses themselves weighed just over a tonne each!

Back in time

The Belgian Draft's ancestors were originally known as Brabants and, until 1940, Belgian and Brabant horses were essentially the same breed. After the Second World War the Brabant was bred to be heavier in Europe, while the Belgian was made taller and lighter-bodied in the USA. Modern Belgian Drafts are usually smaller than European Brabants, but a similar build.

FACT FILE

Home country: Brabant, Belgium
Height: 16.2–17hh
Colours: Light chestnut with a flaxen mane and tail
Uses: Draught, showing and riding

DID YOU KNOW?

Belgian Drafts are the most common breed of draught horse in the USA.

DID YOU KNOW?

The tallest horse in the world is a Belgian Draft called Jake, who stands at 20.2hh, or 2.10m!

TOTALLY TACKTASTIC

See how much you know about tack cleaning

Tack cleaning may not be your fave horsey job, but it's super-important because it'll help keep your saddle and bridle in mint condition. We've got some fun tack cleaning facts to share – tick the ones you already knew, then add up your total to see if you're a tack trainee or cleaning connoisseur!

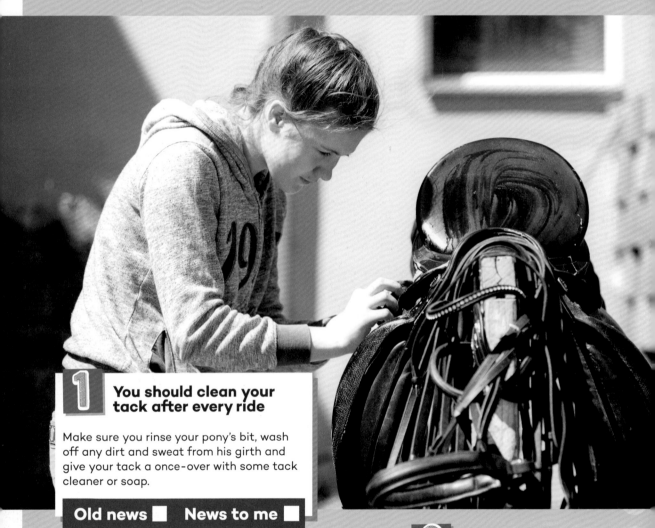

1 You should clean your tack after every ride

Make sure you rinse your pony's bit, wash off any dirt and sweat from his girth and give your tack a once-over with some tack cleaner or soap.

Old news ■ **News to me** ■

2 Toothpaste makes a great metal cleaner

You can use metal polish to make buckles and rings sparkle but, if you don't have any, toothpaste is great alternative!

Old news ■ **News to me** ■

3 You can put bits and stirrup irons in the dishwasher

This will help make them super-shiny! Be sure to ask your parents' permission first, and get rid of any mud on the stirrup irons beforehand.

Old news ■ **News to me** ■

4. Tack can get black blobs of grease called jockeys

These can be caused by a build-up of saddle soap. Don't worry, though, you can rub them away using a course towel or a [pa]d made of horse hair.

Old news ☐   **News to me** ☐

5. Don't use too much soap

[A] little goes a long way, and foamy soap [on] your saddle will just make it sticky and [du]ll-looking, as well as attracting more dirt!

Old news ☐   **News to me** ☐

6. It's a good idea to use different sponges for [d]ifferent stages

[To] prevent you putting dirt back onto your [cl]ean saddle make sure have one cloth for [w]ashing your saddle off, one for the soap [an]d another for polishing.

Old news ☐   **News to me** ☐

7. Give your tack a deep clean every two weeks

[T]his means taking it all apart so you can [cl]ean and condition every nook and cranny. [It]s these hidden-away bits that are often [fir]st to crack.

Old news ☐   **News to me** ☐

8. Wipe over the top of your saddle before a comp

[Yo]u don't want any left over saddle polish [or] soap to stain your light-coloured jods! [S]o, remember to give it a quick wipe with [a] cloth before you get on to make sure it's [s]uper-clean.

Old news ☐   **News to me** ☐

9. Using warm water is better than cold

Warm water cuts through grease more easily than cold water. If you don't have access to hot water at your yard, why not take a thermos with you?

Old news ☐   **News to me** ☐

10. Store your tack in the perfect place

Using a saddle cover and keeping your tack in a cool, dry place will help your cleaning efforts last longer! Allowing it too get too hot or damp can encourage mould to grow and the leather to crack.

Old news ☐   **News to me** ☐

I KNEW...

/10

0-3 Tack trainee
Tack cleaning may be the yard job you dread most but, if you remember these tips for next time, it's sure to make things easier! If you keep at it, your tack will be gleaming in no time.

4-7 Leather learner
You know a few things about tack care, but there's deffo room for improvement. Now you know a few more hints and tricks, you can make sure you tack stays supple and shiny at all times.

8-10 Cleaning connoisseur
Well done! You already knew lots about tack cleaning, so your saddle and bridle are sure to be in peak condition. To make things even more fun, why not clean your tack alongside friends? That way, you can share tips!

ALONG FOR THE RIDE

Race home to the stables before nightfall!

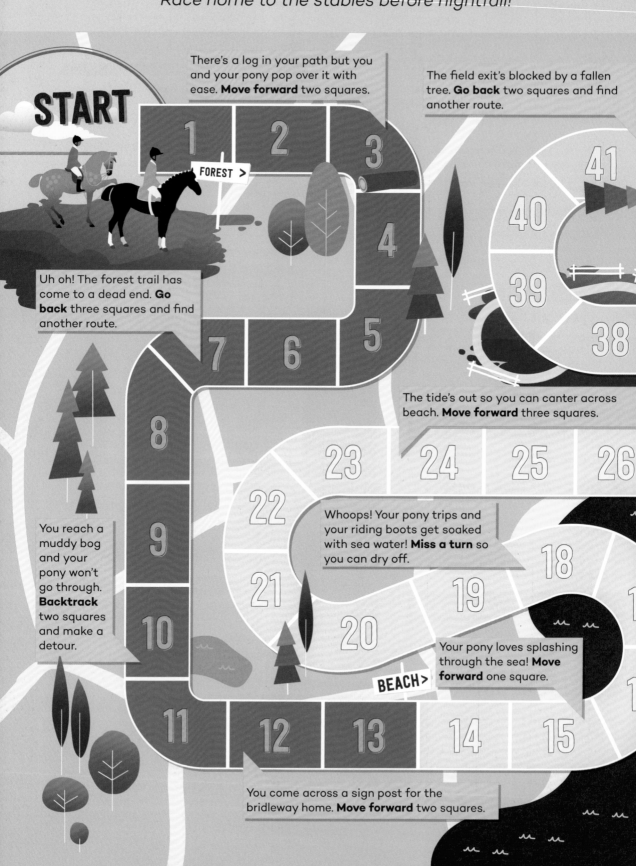

START

There's a log in your path but you and your pony pop over it with ease. **Move forward** two squares.

The field exit's blocked by a fallen tree. **Go back** two squares and find another route.

FOREST >

Uh oh! The forest trail has come to a dead end. **Go back** three squares and find another route.

The tide's out so you can canter across beach. **Move forward** three squares.

You reach a muddy bog and your pony won't go through. **Backtrack** two squares and make a detour.

Whoops! Your pony trips and your riding boots get soaked with sea water! **Miss a turn** so you can dry off.

BEACH >

Your pony loves splashing through the sea! **Move forward** one square.

You come across a sign post for the bridleway home. **Move forward** two squares.

You and your friends have gone for an awesome hack, but you're lost and need to find your way back to the stables before dark. Journey across different terrain, navigate obstacles in your path and avoid getting stuck. Race against your friends to see who can get home first!

WHAT YOU NEED
- a dice
- friends to play with
- a counter per player

HOW TO PLAY
Place your counters at the start and take it in turns to roll the dice (youngest player goes first). Be sure to follow the instructions on the squares you land on. The first player to arrive at the stables is the winner!

N >

There are traffic lights at the entrance to the village. **Miss a turn.**

42   43   44   45   46   47   48

The stables are almost in sight, and your pony walks faster as he recognises his surroundings. **Move forward** two squares.

Your pony's starting to feel tired. Come back to walk and **miss a turn.**

49

37   36   35   34   50   51

HILLS v

You reach a hill that slows your pony's speed. **Go back** two squares.

27

You set off at a gallop. **Move forward** four squares.

28   33   52   53

Almost home! A tractor spooks your pony. **Go back** a square.

29

FINISH

32   54

30   31

PERFECT PACES

Learn all about your pony's gaits

Ponies have four different gaits – walk, trot, canter and gallop. Each one varies in speed and has a different rhythm, so they feel totally unique to ride. From the calm walk you'll have stayed in when you first learnt to ride, to the exhilarating gallop where you feel like you're flying, we've got the lowdown on each and every pace you'll experience.

TOP TIP

Walking on a long rein is a great way to begin and end a session. It'll help stretch out and loosen your pony's muscles, which will help them develop, too.

WONDERFUL WALK

Even though it's the slowest pace, walk shouldn't be underestimated! Riding your pony in walk is key for his fitness and it's also ideal for teaching him new things, such as lateral work. Not to mention, you can even pick up double marks in a dressage test for free walk on a long rein.

Walk has a four-beat rhythm, so you should be able to count 1-2-3-4 as he moves each leg.
  The sequence of legs is right hind, right fore, left hind, left fore.

Time to relax

If your pony's feeling tense in any way, it'll show in his walk. It's super-important that his back muscles stay relaxed, otherwise the tightness will disrupt his rhythm. To get top marks for your walk in a dressage test, your pony should feel calm but active so that his strides are ground-covering and purposeful.
  A good way to help your pony relax is to ride lots of turns and circles during your warm-up. This will help loosen his back muscles and keep his brain engaged, too.

Feeling free

Most dressage tests ask you to ride a free walk. This move is a test of your pony's relaxation and willingness to travel forward. It's so important that it's worth double marks! You'll usually be asked to show it while changing the rein, or sometimes on a circle.
  To ask for a free walk…
1. Start in an active walk in a regular rhythm.
2. Gradually release your reins so they become longer. They should be long enough that your pony can stretch his head and neck forward and down, but not so loose that you no longer have a feel on his mouth.
3. Your pony should stretch his neck lower, with his muzzle seeking forward, walking with purpose in an active stride.

TERRIFIC TROT

Trot can feel a little bouncy to ride, but that's because it has a lift to it that can look really expressive. You'll most often need to rise to the trot, which makes it a great test of balance and your ability to move with your pony, but sitting trot's a fab way to improve your seat and strength, too.

Trot has a two-beat rhythm, which means you should be able to count 1-2-1-2 as he's moving.

The sequence of legs is left fore and right hind together, then right fore and left hind together.

n the diagonal

hen you do rising trot in the arena, you need to make sure u're on the correct diagonal. This means rising out of the ddle when your pony's outside foreleg moves forward, and :ting when it moves back. This will help you and your pony better balanced. You can glance down to check if you're the correct diagonal while you get used to it, but it won't long before you feel it automatically. To change diagonal, for two beats then begin rising again.

pole position

fun way to help improve your pony's trot
to ride him over a line of poles. The poles
ll encourage him to keep an even rhythm
d lift his legs up a little higher so that he
opels himself into the air for a bit longer.
Set up four poles in a line, spaced
1.3m apart, and ride positively over them,
eping your legs wrapped around your
ony's sides and looking up and ahead. For
extra challenge, slightly raise one or both
des of each pole to encourage him to use
body even more.

Up the tempo

In higher level dressage tests, a really impressive move is extended trot. This is where the rider asks the horse to lengthen his strides so they become more ground-covering, and he propels himself forward by creating lots of power with his hindquarters. He must remain in balance and have perfect self-carriage to do it properly. The ultimate test of trot is found in Grand Prix level tests – called passage. This is a super-collected, elevated trot that makes the horse look like he's moving in slow motion!

COOL CANTER

This is one of the smoothest, most versatile gaits you can ride. The ideal canter should make you feel as though you're riding a rocking horse! It's the gait you usually jump from, so helping your pony have a great canter is sure to get you far in lots of disciplines.

Canter has a three-beat rhythm, which means you should be able to count 1-2-3 as he's moving.

Left lead
The sequence of legs is right hind, left hind and right fore together, left fore.

Right lead
The sequence of legs is left hind, right hind and left fore together, right fore.

Left lead   Right lead

All in the aids

To ask your pony to pick up canter...

1. Ride a controlled, active sitting trot.
2. Wait until you reach a corner, then squeeze your inside leg on the girth and place your outside leg behind the girth.
3. Soften your hands to encourage him forward and sit up tall.
4. Your pony should pick up canter straight away. His inside foreleg should be leading – it'll feel awkward and uncomfy otherwise. If he picks up the wrong lead, bring him back to trot and ask again.

Sit still

Even though canter is a faster pace, it's much smoother to sit to than trot. So, to keep your pony comfy, try to sit deep into the saddle and get a feel for his rhythm, so you can move your hips with the motion. This will help prevent you from bouncing on his back and make the gait more enjoyable for both of you.

To help improve your seat, why not book a lunge lesson? As long as you're on a calm, reliable schoolmaster, working in canter without stirrups will help your balance and stability in canter.

TOP TIP
When you're thinking about sitting deep in the saddle, imagine you're sitting on a £10 note that you don't want to blow away!

TOP TIP
Only canter your pony on a hack if you're confident he'll stay calm and not get too excited. It's best to go with another reliable combination, too.

Go the extra mile
Young or unschooled ponies usually struggle to keep their balance in canter, so find corners and circles tricky. The best way to improve a pony's canter is to do it in straight lines as often as you can, at the edge of a field or on a straight bridleway. Building up those miles in canter will naturally help him become more balanced and rhythmical when he's in the school.

TOP TIP
A light seat, taking your weight into your heels and coming out of the saddle, will help your pony move more freely in gallop.

GLEEFUL GALLOP

The fastest pace, gallop is no doubt the most thrilling! The gait of racehorses, only ask for it if you know you have control of your pony and that he'll slow down when you ask him to. But there's nothing like going for a blast to blow out the cobwebs!

Gallop has a four-beat rhythm, which means you should be able to count 1-2-3-4 as he's moving.
Left lead
The sequence of legs is right hind, left hind, right fore, left fore.
Right lead
The sequence of legs is left hind, right hind, left fore, right fore.

Left lead   **Right lead**

In the wild
Ponies are designed to be super-speedy so that, in the wild, they can outrun predators and escape to safety. So, when a pony's galloping, his adrenaline will be super-high. He'll also tire quickly if he's not used to galloping. Ponies often get excited if their riders take them for a blast, but it's a great way to get them fit for cross-country and increase their endurance.

On the field
You can pick up gallop between fences while you're in a cross-country competition to help you get to the finish line as close to the optimum time as possible. However, don't jump from gallop, so you need to teach your pony to come back to you when you ask.

You'll also need to get him gallop fit first, and you can do this using interval training. The best places to go for a gallop are on a specially designed gallop track, or the edge of a field. Gradually increase how much time you spend in gallop, and practise pushing your pony on and back to test your control.

NEAT & TIDY

Does your yard need a spruce-up? Find out how her plus have a fun day with you pals in the process!

Keeping your yard clean and tidy is important for your pony's wellbeing, but you'll feel really proud when you see how amazing it looks, too! Plus, cleaning days don't have to be done alone. Get your pony pals involved and you'll have it done in half the time, and have a ball, too

TOP TIP
Many hands make light work! Give your pals a hand when you're finished or do each stable one at a time – everything's more fun with friends.

Home, sweet home
Your pony can spend quite a lot of time in his stable, so it's important to make it as clean and comfy as possible! Choose a warm day to give it a deep clean, sweeping out any cobwebs and moving the rubber mats to give them a thorough scrub with a pony-friendly disinfectant – don't forget about the floor underneath, too! Lay the mats outside to dry then, once you've popped them back in, set up a fresh bed for your pony to sleep on.

TOP TIP
Rubber mats can be really heavy, so ask an adult to help you.

DID YOU KNOW?

Keeping your pony's stable clean will help his breathing, because dust can affect his airways.

...orage wars

...r tack and feed room can quickly
...ome really dirty, so take a bit of time
...ull everything out and give it a freshen
...Sweep the floor – giving it a scrub with
...e disinfectant if you need to – and brush
...cobwebs away. Loose feed can attract
...ents, but storing all your feed in metal bins
...keep them at bay, so it's worth getting
...r feed room in order!

TOP TIP

Consider some creative storage ideas, like hanging up your numnahs so you can choose your fave colour for the day!

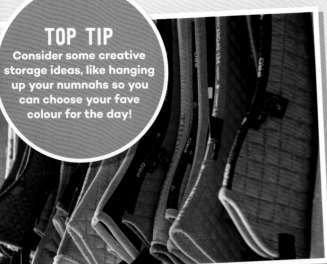

All the gear

One of the best parts of a yard tidy, organising your kit is a great way to work out whether you have everything you need and sell or give away anything you don't. You'll feel super-organised and know you're ready for anything.

First, lay out all your rugs, separating any that don't fit or you don't use, then any that need a wash before they're stored away or used again. Keep the ones you use regularly close to hand, then pack up rugs by season or thickness. Do the same for your tack and riding kit, too. With everything organised, you'll be able to store it neatly and find things more easily.

Field day

Making sure your pony's field is safe is mega-important for his wellbeing. It's not just how much grass he has that matters, either. Here are a few things you should check...

- ☑ all the fencing is secure and there aren't any bits sticking out that he could hurt himself on
- ☑ his shelter's in good working order, with no nails or pieces of wood sticking out
- ☑ there aren't any poisonous plants – dig them out with the help of an adult if you spot any!
- ☑ his water trough is clean and full of fresh water
- ☑ whether any areas have become poached or overgrazed. Speak to your yard owner about strip grazing to give the land a break
- ☑ there isn't leftover hay the ponies won't eat laying around. Grab a wheelbarrow and clear it up if there is

ABOVE THE REST

Hannah's determined to prove that her unusual horse is the best of the bunch

Hannah and her parents lived on Sunnydown Farm in Lincolnshire. They kept a flock of sheep as well as seven chickens, two pygmy goats and a rescue pig named Gertrude. But Hannah's favourite animal of all was Henry the Suffolk Punch. He was a whopping 17.2hh, and super-chunky with a stunning chestnut coat.

Lots of love

Hannah's mum had owned Henry since she was a teenager, and he was in his twenties now. Henry lived with Hannah's Shetland, Digby, who they'd bought to keep him company. The pair were best friends, despite their huge height difference! Hannah absolutely adored the two ponies, but she had a big soft spot for Henry. He was the most gentle giant you'd ever meet, and Hannah spent hours standing on a footstool, lovingly grooming his coat while he dozed.

Hannah loved horses more than anything, but she'd never had much of an interest in riding them. She was a carer at heart, so just enjoyed pampering them and watching them going about their business. She loved drawing, too – there were hundreds of pictures she'd created of Henry plastered across her bedroom wall. She dreamed of being an equine artist one day.

> ❝ Hannah had never listened to anyone else's opinion before and wasn't about to start now ❞

Mean words

One day, Hannah was sitting in class drawing a picture of Henry while she waited for the teacher to arrive and start the lesson. Some of her classmates owned ponies, too, but they all rode competitively at Pony Club. "Are you going to come to the jumping rally on your tiny Shetland then, Hannah?" sneered Melissa. Hannah shrugged off the comment and carried on with her drawing "I don't get why you don't ride," Melissa continued, now joined by another girl, Sarah. "I just don't, okay?" Hannah put her head down and tried to ignore them. "It's because she has weird ponies," Sarah chimed in. "Yeah, why don't you have a normal one to ride?" Melissa laughed. Hannah was saved as the teacher walked in and told everyone to take their

seats. She tried not to let a tear slip as she put away her drawing.

A chance to shine

When Hannah got home that evening, she slumped down at the kitchen table while her mum was cooking. "Look what I picked up from the feed shop today, Hannah," Mum called. Hannah glanced over at a leaflet with *Vale Spring Show* written across the front. Normally she'd have been really excited, but she still felt dejected about the comments Melissa and Sarah had made about Henry and Digby. "I thought it might be fun to take the boys – do something different with them," Hannah's mum continued. "We could enter Digby in the miniatures class, and Henry in rare breeds!" Before she could stop herself, Hannah burst into tears. Her mum rushed over and gave her a hug. Hannah sobbed as she explained what the girls at school had said about the horses being weird. "And they're sure to be at that show laughing at me," she sniffed. Hannah's mum rubbed her back in sympathy. "Well, all the more reason to go and prove them wrong. We'll scrub the boys up so they look their best! Don't let some jealous girls stop you from having fun." Hannah wiped her eyes and smiled. Her mum was right. She'd never listened to anyone else's opinion before and she wasn't about to start now.

Practice makes perfect

Over the next week, Hannah and her mum practised leading Henry and Digby around the field to work out a routine they could do at the show in front of the judges. Digby was a bit naughty and tried to eat grass the whole time, but Henry loved the attention and let Hannah lead him wherever she wanted. He had such massive trot strides that Hannah had to run really fast to keep up!

The night before the show, Hannah's mum and dad helped plait up Henry. He had so much mane that it was a bit of a mammoth task, but Henry was in his element, loving every second of being pampered. Hannah couldn't wait for everyone at the show to see how handsome he was.

...ow day

...nah was so excited that she jumped out of bed the ...ute she heard the cockerel call. Her mum joined her ...he barn to get ready to load the trailer – she'd been ...ate cleaning a special surprise for Henry to wear at ... show.

...When they arrived at the showground, Hannah took ...oment to soak up the atmosphere. There were ...ies and trailers everywhere and it was buzzing with ...different types of ponies. Hannah and her parents ...to work tacking up Henry in his amazing show ...r. He had a freshly polished set of blinkers, and a ...geous collar that made him look like a true working ...vy horse. They even put little ribbons, called flights, ...is mane. He looked unbelievably handsome and ...nah couldn't believe he was really theirs.

...winning performance

...ry's class was first, so Hannah and her mum led ... over to the ring while her dad brought Digby along ...vatch. The pair were dressed in tweed jackets and ...am jodhpurs – they looked almost as good as ...ry did! As they walked across the showground, ...nah couldn't help but notice all the onlookers stop ...d stare at his amazing presence. Everyone was in ... of him and Hannah was filled with pride.

...They entered the ring and joined the other ...npetitors in the rare breeds class, but Hannah ...uldn't help noticing none of the others looked ...impressive as Henry. There was a cute Fjord – a ...rwegian breed with a spikey black-and-blonde ...ne – but none of the others caught Hannah's eye. ...wever, last to enter the ring was Sarah – one of the

girls who'd teased Hannah at school. She was leading Jet – her striking Fell pony – but her face fell when she took in the sight of Henry towering above the rest.

Henry sensed he was the centre of attention and began to float in walk and trot while everyone paraded around in front of the judge. To Hannah's amazement, they were chosen to go to the front of the line-up for inspection. She had butterflies as the judge asked them questions about Henry, then watched closely while they performed the in-hand routine they'd prepared – Henry behaved impeccably.

Sure enough, Henry was picked to win! Hannah and her mum couldn't believe it, as it meant they'd also qualified for the county show! Hannah looked over at Sarah, who gave her a wave – she'd come fifth with Jet and looked very sheepish.

A great day

Digby did well in his class, too, but trod on the judge's foot, which lost him some marks! By the end of the day, Hannah had so many people coming up to her and asking all about Henry that her mouth hurt from smiling. Even Sarah came over, joined begrudgingly by Melissa, to compliment her. They both apologised for doubting Henry and Digby before, and gave Henry a cuddle, as everyone who met him fell in love with him.

Hannah was so pleased she'd come to the show because she'd discovered Henry's true talents! He was born to be in the spotlight and Hannah was really excited to show him off at more shows. From that day on, Melissa and Sarah were much nicer to her at school, too, which was a huge bonus! Maybe they weren't so bad after all.

BRILLIANT BARREL RACING

Learn more about the USA's most awesome equine sport

Mega-fast and super-exciting, barrel racing is a rodeo sport mainly done in the USA. It involves speeding around a clover-leaf pattern of barrels in the fastest time and is a huge test of a horse's athleticism and training, as well as the rider's skills and balance.

Back in time

Barrel racing has been around for decades and is a huge part of American horsey culture. It was originally a sport for women and the first governing body, the Women's Professional Rodeo Association (WPRA), was formed in 1948. Initially, it was called the Girls Rodeo Association (GRA) and had just 74 members, with only around 60 approved events. In comparison, British Eventing has nearly 200 fixtures per year! The group was set up to help women feel more welcome in rodeo events, including barrel racing, and changed its name to the WPRA in 1981. It continues to provide women with the chance to compete in rodeo events today.

Into the ring

Nowadays, barrel racing's part of rodeos at all levels and for all ages and abilities. Competitions usually group riders by age, but there are events with open barrel racing jackpots that welcome competitors of any age or gender.

Events are timed with an electric eye, which uses lasers to record times a bit like in showjumping classes, or by a judge who drops a flag to start or stop the timer. The riders enter the ring at full speed through a tunnel, triggering the timer en-route to the first barrel and stopping it once they've finished the route. There's a five-second penalty for knocking a barrel and a 60-second time limit to complete the whole course, so speed is the name of the game!

DID YOU KNOW?

The first-ever competitive barrel racing event is believed to have been held in Texas.

PONY recommends you wear an up-to-standard riding hat when mounted at all times

DID YOU KNOW?

Riders have to dress in a long-sleeved western shirt, western cut trousers or jeans and boots. They even have to follow the dress code for an hour before they compete!

DID YOU KNOW?

Originally, barrel racing events alternated between a figure of eight and the trickier clover-leaf pattern used today.

DID YOU KNOW?

The National Barrel Horse Association UK is bringing barrel racing across the Atlantic, so you could even have a go yourself!

The perfect pony

American Quarter Horses are most commonly used for barrel racing because they're strong, agile and super-speedy over short distances. In fact, they're considered the fastest breed over a quarter of a mile – hence their name.

Top-quality barrel racing horses can easily be worth US$25,000 – the most expensive ever sold at public auction was for US$68,000!

JOB lot

Find out which equine career path you're destined for

There are lots of different of equine jobs you can choose from. So, if you want to work with horses one day, take our fun quiz to find out which one you'd suit best!

1. What's the best thing about ponies?

○ **a)** Grooming them until they're super-shiny

○ **b)** Riding them, obvs!

○ **c)** Learning loads about them

○ **d)** Caring for and bonding with them

2. Which three words describe you the best?

○ **a)** Sporty, motivated, competitive

○ **b)** Creative, fun, bubbly

○ **c)** Logical, organised, meticulous

○ **d)** Kind, caring, patient

3. Which of these non-horsey jobs do you think you'd like most?

○ **a)** Stylist

○ **b)** Teacher

○ **c)** Doctor

○ **d)** Firefighter

4. Which of these would you look for most in a future job?

○ **a)** Something that can help me further my skills and push me to the very top of my game

○ **b)** Having the chance to share my knowledge with others

○ **c)** A job where I'm always learning new things about ponies

○ **d)** Something rewarding, where I feel like I'm helping my fave animal

5. What kind of pony would you most like to own?

○ **a)** An established competition pony who's super-stunning

○ **b)** A well-behaved schoolmaster who could teach me loads about riding

○ **c)** A foal to care for!

○ **d)** A scruffy one who's a work in progress, so I could train him up myself and give him a good life!

What's your best quality?

a) I'm energetic and super-motivated

b) I'm good with people and love to help my friends with their problems

c) I have an eye for detail and like everything to be done perfectly

d) I'm cool in a crisis and super-patient

What kinds of ponies would you like to work with?

a) Smart competition ones with loads of talent and ability

b) Super-cute ones who love to be cuddled

c) Sick or injured ponies who I can nurse back to health

d) Nervous rescue ponies whose confidence I can help rebuild

If you had the chance to own a yard one day, what would you enjoy most?

a) Getting to exercise loads of amazing horses for the liveries

b) Organising fun yard activities for pony-loving children

c) Being able to make sure all the ponies are being looked after in the best way possible

d) Having the space to rescue ponies who need good homes

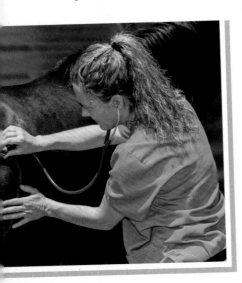

Mostly As — COMPETITION GROOM

You're destined to work at a super-successful competition yard! Whether your passion's dressage, showjumping or eventing, you never shy away from a challenge and always want to improve your skills. You'll need to be highly organised to keep all the horses in peak condition and your plaiting skills will be second to none. You're sure to thrive in this fast-paced environment, and you might even get to rub shoulders with some of the greats!

Other jobs you'd suit:
- pro rider
- polo groom
- jockey
- stud hand
- event organiser

Mostly Bs — RIDING INSTRUCTOR

You'd make an awesome riding instructor! You have loads of brilliant ideas to keep things fresh and fun for your pupils, and you just love the cute and cuddly ponies involved, too! You'll need to have a talent for explaining, tons of riding knowledge and be really inventive and creative so everyone wants to come to you for more lessons!

Other jobs you'd suit:
- equine college lecturer
- yard manager
- horse trainer
- sports psychologist
- BHS assessor

Mostly Cs — VETERINARY NURSE

It's your destiny to be an equine vet nurse! You'll need to run a tight ship to make sure all the in-patients get the treatments they need, and the yard is kept spick and span at all times. You'll have excellent knowledge of equine wounds and ailments so you can get your pony patients back in tip-top condition. Your eye for detail and skills means you'd deffo be up for the job.

Other jobs you'd suit:
- equine vet
- physiotherapist
- equine dental technician
- farrier
- saddle fitter

Mostly Ds — EQUINE WELFARE OFFICER

You'd be a fab equine welfare officer! You're super-kind and caring so would be ideal to help soothe nervous rescue ponies in need. You're committed to helping them recover and finding them perfect partners for rehoming down the line. You're patient and level-headed, which are perfect qualities for when you need to come to a pony's rescue!

Other jobs you'd suit:
- rehabilitation groom
- behaviourist
- equine communications officer
- mounted police officer

TOTALLY IN SYNC

Jazz up your schooling sesh by riding super sequences

Ever get a little lonely schooling by yourself? Well, why not ride with a friend? There are loads of ways you can school your ponies together and it has lots of benefits, too. We've put together some fab moves you can practise first, then link up, to make an impressive synchronised sequence!

TOP TIP
It's a good idea to ride with other ponies that you know yours gets along with, like one of his field buddies.

1 Centre stage

This move is an easy one to start with. You need to stay totally straight, and it's a good way to get the ponies used to working together.

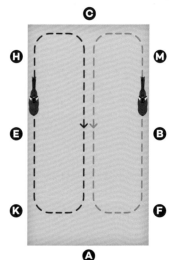

How to ride it

1. Walk the ponies around the outside of the arena on opposite reins.
2. Start the move with one pony at E the other at B.
3. Walk towards C at the same pace, keeping an eye on the other rider to make sure you're level.
4. Both riders should turn just before C at exactly the same moment and ride down the centre line side-by-side.
5. When you reach D, turn away from each other and ride large again.
6. If the ponies find the exercise easy in walk, have a go in trot.

2 Inside out

This is a great way to spice up your circles! Whoever rides in the centre will have to do the most bending and you'll need to ride really accurately, too.

How to ride it

1. Begin by trotting large on opposite reins.
2. Come onto a circle in the middle of the arena. One rider should ride the 20m circle, while the other goes slightly smaller, onto the 15m circle.
3. Once you've passed each other two or three times, return to the track and ride large.
4. Change the rein and have a go the other way. You can switch up who rides the smaller circle, too.

Up the challenge

If your ponies are nailing the exercise in trot, why not have a go in canter?

3 Pair shaped

Not only will this help supple up your pony, it'll also challenge his rhythm because you'll need to stay at the exact same speed as the other rider!

How to ride it

1. Start by riding large on opposite reins.
2. Line up at B and E and head towards C.
3. Turn just before C and come onto opposing 10m circles. You'll ride side-by-side for the first part of the circle, then away from each other to continue the circle towards the long side.
4. Stay completely level with each other, so you can join up side-by-side again when you return to the centre line.
5. Ride the circles once more, then join together and ride down the centre line to finish.

TOP TIP
Don't forget to communicate with each other while you're practising. If you talk about what you're doing as you go, it will help you stay in sync.

Loop-de-loop

This exercise will really test your accuracy as a rider, and your pony will need to listen closely to your aids.

How to ride it

1. Start the exercise in the same way as in exercise one.
2. Ride down the centre line side-by-side.
3. When you reach G, split off and ride a 5m loop. You should stay level with each other, and arrive at the three-quarter line when you're in line with X.
4. Loop back again so that you meet at D and become side-by-side again.
5. Head down the centre line two abreast, then split off and ride large in opposite directions to finish.

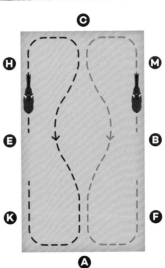

5 Snazzy snake

This exercise is a real test of your co-ordination with each other, and it's a fun suppling exercise to try, too.

How to ride it

1. Walk large on the right rein, with one rider on the track and the other next to them on the inside track.
2. Begin your first half circle at C. The rider on the outside will need to ride a slightly larger circle than the rider on the inside.

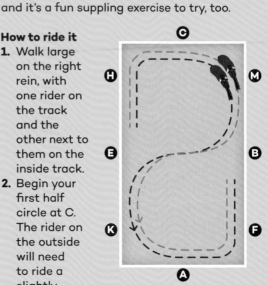

3. Ride straight over X, then switch, so the rider who was on the outside now becomes on the inside.
4. Ride the last half circle with the new outside rider making a slightly larger circle than the rider on the inside,
5. Ride large again when you reach A and have another go.

Up the challenge

Once you've worked out where you both need to be, you can have a go at the exercise in trot. Make sure you still go at exactly the same speed, though! You can also be clever and join two snake shapes up to ride a full figure-of-eight. This is pretty tricky, though, as you'll need to keep swapping who goes on the inside!

Link it up

Once you and your friend have each move nailed individually, why not link them together to create an awesome sequence? You could even ride it to music to make it look more impressive!

Grand finale

Don't forget to halt and salute to finish your display! It looks super-cute, but it can be tricky to get both ponies standing perfectly side-by-side, and square, too.

FACT OR FICTION

Can you tell the truth from a fib? Find out with our true or false quiz

TURN TO P100 TO FIND OUT HOW YOU GOT ON!

A re you a pony know-it-all or do you need to brush up your knowledge? Test yourself – and compare your results with friends – to see how much you really know about your pony pals.

1. **To be classed as a pony an equine needs to be under 15hh.**

   FACT ● FICTION ●

2. **Ponies can't be sick!**

   FACT ● FICTION ●

3. **Chestnut mares are more likely to be moody than other colours.**

   FACT ● FICTION ●

4. **Cobs are a breed of horse.**

   FACT ● FICTION ●

5. **White hooves are weaker than dark ones.**

   FACT ● FICTION ●

6. **Ponies can't see pinks, but they can see blues and greens.**

   FACT ● FICTION ●

7. **Young ponies are called yearlings until they're three years old.**

   FACT ● FICTION ●

8. **The best way to work out the age of your pony is to check his teeth.**

   FACT ● FICTION ●

9. Foals are up and walking within a few hours of being born.

FACT ⬤ FICTION ⬤

10. You shouldn't clean your tack more than once a month.

FACT ⬤ FICTION ⬤

11. Ponies prefer to live in groups of friends.

FACT ⬤ FICTION ⬤

12. A healthy pony will live up to a maximum of 15 years.

FACT ⬤ FICTION ⬤

13. Horses, ponies, donkeys, mules and zebras are all called equines.

FACT ⬤ FICTION ⬤

14. The area where your pony's girth sits is called the withers.

FACT ⬤ FICTION ⬤

15. Grey ponies are usually a darker colour as foals.

FACT ⬤ FICTION ⬤

16. The part of a bridle that goes behind your pony's ears is called the headband.

FACT ⬤ FICTION ⬤

17. A white mark that goes up to your pony's knee is called a stocking.

FACT ⬤ FICTION ⬤

18. Racehorses are almost always Connemaras.

FACT ⬤ FICTION ⬤

19. There are four inches in a hand.

FACT ⬤ FICTION ⬤

20. You always mount and dismount from the left-hand side.

FACT ⬤ FICTION ⬤

I SCORED

/20

HORSE SHOE DECORATION

Create this beautiful hanging horseshoe decoration!

YOU'LL NEED

- ✓ Horseshoes
- ✓ Paintbrush
- ✓ Primer
- ✓ Paints
- ✓ String

TOP TIP

You could paint your pony's name onto the horseshoe.

...lean the
...es carefully
...n soapy
...er and a pan
...urer.

Ask an adult for help with cleaning.

2. Paint an undercoat onto the shoes with the primer to give a better painting surface.

3. Choose your base coat colour and paint it onto the shoes. This is the background colour you'll then paint patterns onto.

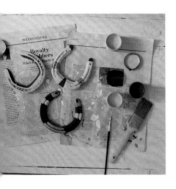

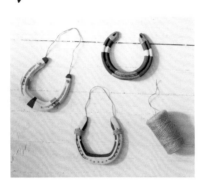

...Use the other colours to paint ...patterns and stripes onto the ...es – be as creative as you like!

5. Tie a piece of string around the ends of each shoe to make a loop. Make sure you tie it tight!

6. Hang up your shoes wherever you'd like – in the tack room, outside your pony's stable or even in your bedroom!

TOP TIP
Make sure you hang the shoe securely so it doesn't fall down!

LOOKING GOOD!
Spice up your walls with these stunning shoes!

FRIENDLY FACES

PART TWO

Does Sunny make friends at her and Amy's new yard? Find out here...

Gem as **Ginger**

Ruby and Dilly as
Amy and **Sunny**

Lily and Penny as
Helena and **Pickle**

Hollie and Moon as
Ellie and **Blue**

Dream as
Flight

LATER THAT DAY

Wow! Where are we now? You don't mind if I hide behind you, right?

Where are all the ponies? I hope I won't be lonely here.

Of course I'm a good girl! Maybe not on competition day, though...

Easy to ride? Amy taught me everything I know!

... This is really boring, though.

WOAH!

Nooo! Pickle, I hate dogs!

THE END

FESS UPS

Have a chuckle at these cheeky ponies' cringey confessions!

Downgraded

I should tell you, my fave thing in the world is jumping. I looove to jump anything and everything – especially if there's a crowd watching. I like to think of myself as a sports horse and often boast to the other ponies about how good I am at everything.

But one day, my rider, Lydia, brought a small child with her to the yard. She tacked me up while the child watched – I thought it meant we must be doing something really fun to impress her. Then, before I knew it, Lydia had plonked the child onto my back and started leading me around like a riding school pony! It was sooo humiliating and all the other ponies were laughing at me from the field!

Horrace

WHOOPS!

KINDA CRINGE

SOOOO C...

CRINGE-O-METER

Into the blue

One summer evening, my owner, Melissa, took me for a beach ride. My bestie Chipmunk and his rider came along, too. We cantered through the surf and it was loads of fun! I was a bit scared of the splashy waves at first, but I followed Chipmunk and got used to the feeling of the water against my legs. Then, I caught sight of something bobbing up and down in the water – *it must be a pony-eating shark!* I jumped into the air and cantered sideways to get myself back to safety. Then, I heard Chipmunk whinny to me. It turned out it was just a piece of seaweed – whoops, my bad!

Silver

mp for joy

rider, Harry, and I were at a dressage comp,
d I was feeling bored. I don't like dressage
y much, and just wanted to go home to
field buddies. When it was our turn to
rt the test, I could sense Harry tense with
ves, which put me on edge. I trotted round
e arena and was completely startled by the
dge honking their horn! I leapt up in the air
d jumped over the white board that marked
e edge of the arena. Then I cantered off
d popped over another one as well! I always
eferred showjumping to dressage, but Harry
dn't seem too pleased!

uzzle

Greedy guts

It was early one morning
and there wasn't a soul
on the yard. All my friends were tucking into
what was left of their haynets, but I'd already
guzzled down all of mine. I was feeling a bit
peckish so scanned the barn. My eyes landed
on a tasty bucket of feed that my owner,
Penny, had left out for my breakfast. I couldn't
wait until she arrived to feed me so decided
to take matters into my own hooves. I grabbed
the stable bolt between my teeth and slid it
across to let myself out. I went and munched
my breakfast, then started tucking into a
nearby hay bale, too. Unfortunately, Penny
turned up shortly after and caught me red
hooved - whoops!

Daisy

Separation anxiety

I'd just got back from a really fun ride with
my loaner, Peter. I was a bit late going out
into my field by the time he'd untacked me
and sponged me off. Peter led me out to
my regular paddock, but it looked like my
best friend in the world, Sonny, wasn't out,
which seemed very suspicious. I looked round
anxiously, wondering where he was. I whinnied
and whinnied, frantically pacing up and down
the fence line. Then, I noticed a tail swish from
behind a tree – he was asleep in the shade! So
he *had* been there the whole time, I just hadn't
noticed... LOL!

Prince

Walk of shame

I was munching my haynet when I noticed a
trailer pull up next to barn. Then, my owner,
Denise, appeared and started wrapping
some boot things onto my legs, which felt
strange – they came all the way up over my
knees! When she tried to lead me towards
the trailer, I stood still as a statue because I
felt like I couldn't walk in these weird things!
Then, when she tugged on my leadrope, I
took some steps forward, but couldn't help
flailing my legs about crazily in the process.
All the other ponies, as well as Denise,
started laughing at my funny walk!

Trixie

THE *big* THREE

Find out how to check your pony's vital signs with our handy guide

Temperature, pulse and respiration rates are three super-important parts of your pony's health. Knowing what's normal for him will help you keep track of his health and spot any changes that could mean he's feeling under the weather. The sooner you notice he's not feeling his best, the sooner he'll be able to get treatment and start feeling better.

Beat the heat

A pony's temperature should be 37.2–38.3°C. If it's higher than this it could mean he's poorly with an infection and you'll need to call the vet straight away.

The best way to check his temperature is by inserting a thermometer with a bit of petroleum jelly on the end into his rectum. Always stand to the side in case he gets upset and lifts a leg, and don't remove the thermometer until you hear a beep.

TOP TIP
Make sure you check your pony's temp regularly and at different times of day so you know what's normal for him. Why not keep a diary to help you remember?

> *The sooner you notice he's not feeling his best, the sooner he'll be able to get treatment*

Breathe easy

Laboured breaths can mean that your pony's in pain or having difficulty breathing. He should take 10–20 breaths per minute at rest, but this will increase while he's working, so make sure he's relaxed when you check it.

To work out his respiration rate, watch your pony's ribcage and count the number of breaths he takes for 30 seconds. You can then double this to get the number of breaths he takes per minute. Another method is to hold your hand near his nostrils and feel his breaths rather than looking for them.

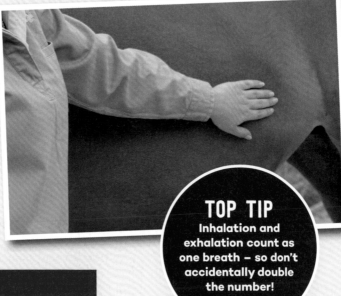

TOP TIP
Inhalation and exhalation count as one breath – so don't accidentally double the number!

Heart to heart

Your pony's resting heart rate should be 28–44 beats per minute (BPM). Any higher can mean he's in pain, scared or unwell.

If you have a stethoscope, you can place it on your pony's ribs just behind his left elbow to count how many beats you hear in 30 seconds. You can then double it to find out the beats per minute. If you don't have a stethoscope, cup your hand under his jaw and use two fingers to feel for the artery that runs between his jaw bones. This can be quite tricky, so if you're struggling ask your yard manager or instructor to show you how to find it. You should be able to feel a pulse when gently pressing down on it. Again, count how many beats you feel over 30 seconds, then double it.

DID YOU KNOW?
A super-fit pony will have a lower resting pulse because each heartbeat will pump more blood, meaning his heart doesn't need to work so fast.

DID YOU KNOW?
Your pony's gums should look pink and feel moist to touch if he's healthy, so it's worth checking them regularly.

Little 'n' Large

DARTMOORS AND CLYDESDALES

Two very different breeds to read about!

Daring Dartmoors

A hardy breed thanks to the tough conditions on its home turf, Dartmoor ponies have excellent stamina, making them great working ponies. Historically, they were used by tin miners and quarry workers. But, despite their usefulness, the breed's on the decline. In 1900 there were around 5,000 ponies, but that number's just 300 today.

It's thought that domesticated ponies have lived on Dartmoor for more than 500 years, but they've likely lived on the moor as wild ponies for a lot longer. In the 1900s Arab, Welsh and Fell pony bloodlines were added to the Dartmoor ponies, which have led to the tough yet smart pony that's so popular all over the UK.

FACT FILE

Home country: Devon, England
Height: 11.1–13hh
Colours: Bay, brown, black, grey, chestnut and roan
Uses: Riding and driving

Super-cool Clydesdales

In the mid-18th Century Flemish stallions were imported to Scotland to breed larger horses – creating the ancestors of the incredible Clydesdales we know and love today. The first use of the name Clydesdale was recorded in 1826, and in the Clydesdale Horse Society of Scotland was formed in 1877. The new breed was so popular that 20,183 horses were exported between 1884 and 1945!

Originally, Clydesdales were bred to be compact and strong, smaller than Shires and Belgian Drafts. However, in the 1940s taller horses were bred to look more impressive in parades, which is why Clydesdales are so tall today.

DID YOU KNOW?

More than 25,000 Clydesdales were registered in Australia between 1924 and 2008, and it's known as the breed that built Australia.

FACT FILE

Home country: Clydesdale, Scotland
Height: 16–18hh
Colours: Bay, black, grey and chestnut. Most also have white markings
Uses: Driving, riding and showing

DID YOU KNOW?

Thanks to their chilled-out temperament, Clydesdales are used as drum horses by the British Household Cavalry!

DID YOU KNOW?

Dartmoor ponies have been granted rare breed status.

DID YOU KNOW?

The first Dartmoor studbook was formed by the Polo Pony Society in 1898!

FROM HEAD TO TOE

Name the parts of a pony!

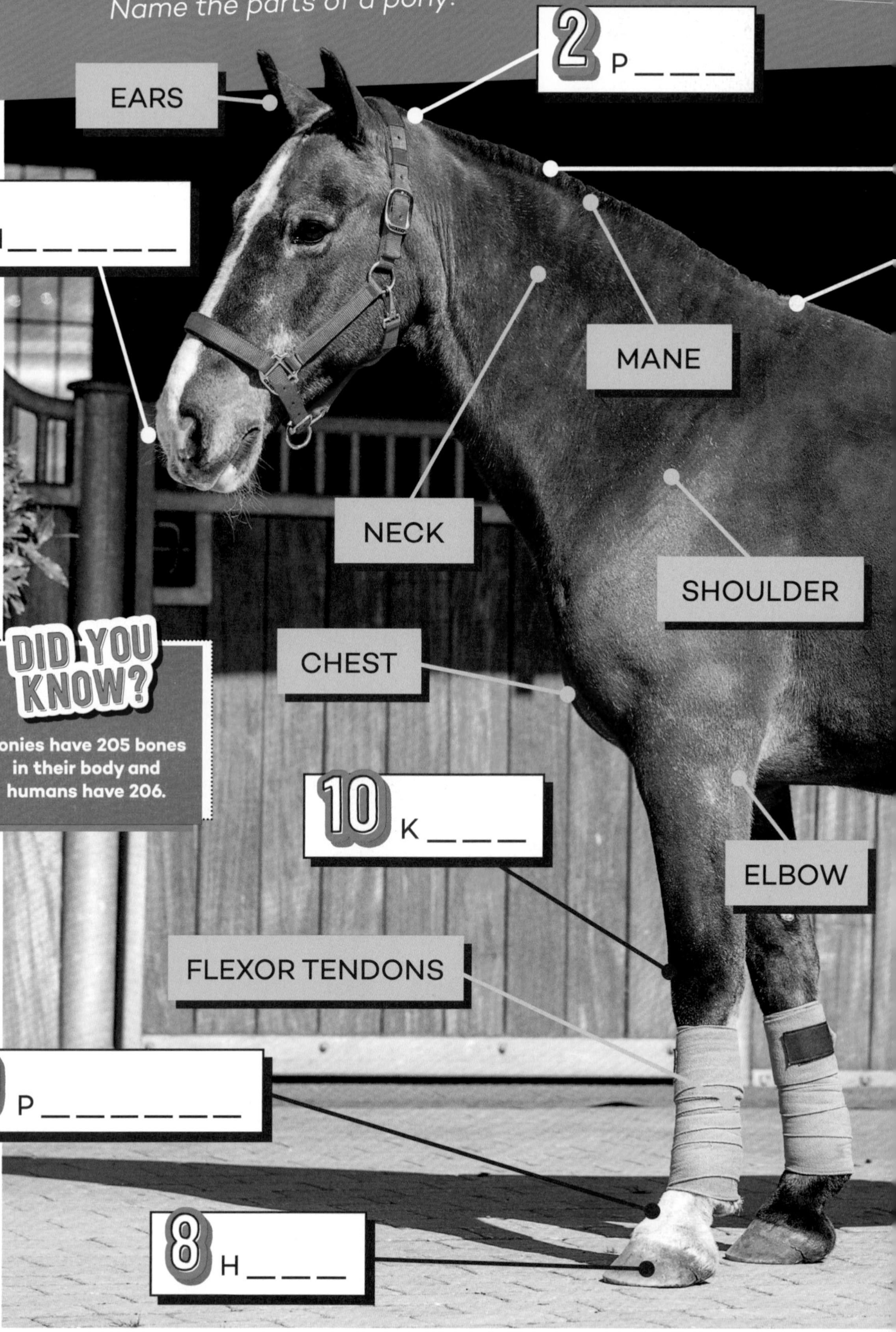

2 P _ _ _ _

EARS

1 M _ _ _ _ _ _ _

MANE

NECK

SHOULDER

DID YOU KNOW?

Ponies have 205 bones in their body and humans have 206.

CHEST

10 K _ _ _ _

ELBOW

FLEXOR TENDONS

9 P _ _ _ _ _ _ _ _

8 H _ _ _ _

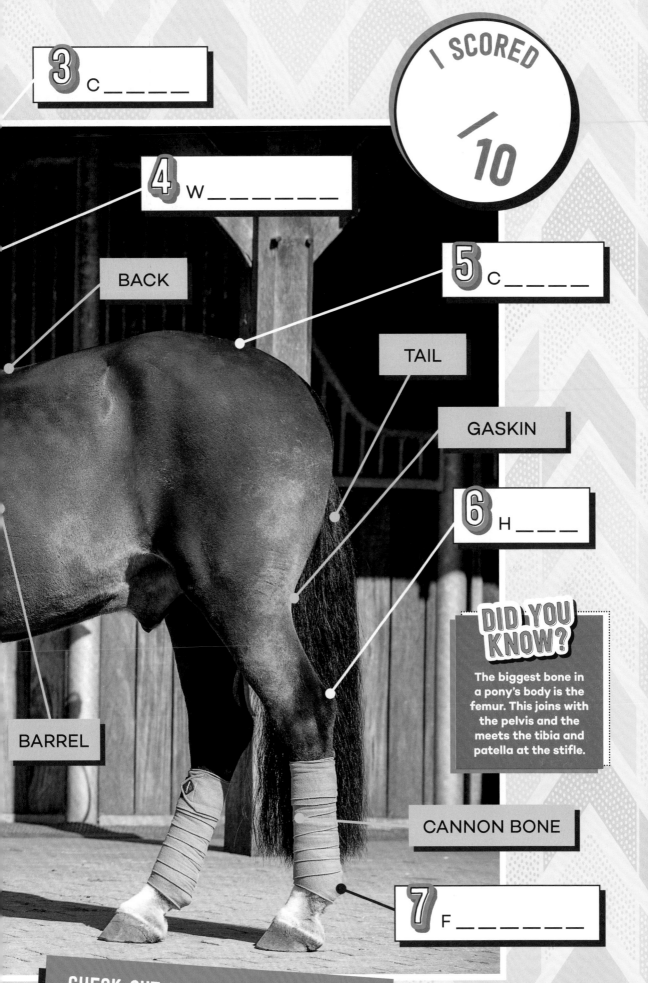

3 C _ _ _ _ _

4 W _ _ _ _ _ _ _

BACK

5 C _ _ _ _ _

TAIL

GASKIN

6 H _ _ _ _

DID YOU KNOW?

The biggest bone in a pony's body is the femur. This joins with the pelvis and the meets the tibia and patella at the stifle.

BARREL

CANNON BONE

7 F _ _ _ _ _ _ _

CHECK OUT P100 FOR THE ANSWERS

SPECTACULAR SNOW POLO

The definition of fast and furious, this game is super-exciting for riders and spectators alike

Snow polo's a crazy-cool version of the well-known game of polo that's played on grass. The difference is the pitch's surface – usually a frozen lake that's covered in snow. Constantly growing in popularity, particularly in the ski towns of Europe and the USA, this awesome sport has plenty of excitement to offer.

PONY recommends you wear an up-to-standard riding hat when mounted at all times

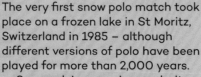

Back in time

The very first snow polo match took place on a frozen lake in St Moritz, Switzerland in 1985 – although different versions of polo have been played for more than 2,000 years.

Snow polo's grown in popularity over the years, with games taking place in Italy, France, Austria, Spain, Germany and, more recently, Argentina, Russia and the USA. In 2011, China hosted the very first snow polo match in Asia.

The 37th snow polo World Cup will take place in St Moritz in January 2022. Just like the first-ever match that happened there, the World Cup will run on the town's frozen lake.

Regular polo fields are 180x270m, while snow polo pitches are 155x70m. The field's smaller to accommodate the higher altitude and snow.

Change the game

Snow polo's played over 4–6 chukkas, each six minutes long. The ponies have to be swapped every chukka and each one can only be ridden twice during the game.

Unlike polo played on grass, snow polo has three players on each team. The mallet's always held in the rider's right hand, which makes it easier to hit the ball on the pony's off (or right-hand) side. Much like standard polo, the riders aim to hit the ball into the opposing team's net.

DID YOU KNOW?

Ponies' manes are hogged and their tails plaited up during a game to avoid hair getting caught in the mallets.

Equine athletes

The polo ponies used in any version of the game are usually around 15.1hh, although some are as tall as 16hh. Despite being mostly Thoroughbred crosses and horse-sized, they're called ponies due to their agility. In the USA, Thoroughbreds are often crossed with Quarter Horses to make the ultimate polo pony. Meanwhile, in Argentina Thoroughbred Criollo crosses reign supreme and Australian stock horses are most popular down under.

The ponies are trained to be brave and unfazed by the ball, mallet and other ponies bumping into them. They're also taught to respond to neck-reining, which means the riders can hold the reins in one hand and still be able to turn at speed.

IN THE SPOTLIGHT

Signs your pony's a natural born star

O f course you know your fave pony's the bee's knees, but was he secretly born to be in the public eye? If he loves performing in front of a crowd and being the centre of attention, then he may have the potential to be a real pony celeb! Here are some signs your fave pony has the wow factor, and was born to be in the spotlight.

☐ HE'S SUPER-TALENTED, BUT A TOTAL DIVA

If your pony has true star quality, then it shines through whenever he performs. Whether he's training at home or competing at a show, on a good day he seems to make everything feel easy and effortless. However, he has no qualms about stopping at a fence or throwing in a buck if he's just not feeling it one day – it's his way or the highway!

HE KNOWS HOW TO GET YOUR ATTENTION

[Y]ur fave pony loooooooves being the apple of [y]our eye, and isn't happy if he's being ignored [in] any way. He'll scrape the floor, bang the [sta]ble door, whinny or even squeal to get your [at]tention. He revels in receiving praise and [lov]es it even more if people are watching.

HE THINKS HE CAN OUTSMART YOU

A pony who has that competitive edge is often [s]uper-intelligent – even if it means he's too [c]lever for his own good! He doesn't miss a trick, [s]o you've got to pay extra-close attention [t]hat you've bolted his stable door or tied him [u]p properly, otherwise he's sure to take the [o]pportunity to escape! He always knows when [y]ou have a treat in your pocket, too, and won't [s]top nudging until you hand it over.

HE MAKES PEOPLE LAUGH

In order to be the centre of attention, your pony has no shame in pulling funny faces, doing weird things or getting up to mischief! He loves being the comedian of the yard, whether he's doing a bow or pushing you into a pile of poo with his nose! He lives to entertain and, even though sometimes you're the punchline of his jokes, you can't help but laugh along with him.

HE'S ABSOLUTELY STUNNING AND KNOWS IT

Your pony's fully aware of how beautiful he is! He knows that, even if he's a little bit cheeky, you can't stay cross with him for long because he's just so cute. He always poses perfectly for photos so his shiny coat catches the light just right – in fact, he often looks better in pics than you do! Even if he rolls in mud or has stable stains on him, his gorgeous presence and impressive stance means he looks breathtaking regardless.

HIS PACES ARE TO DIE FOR

A pony with star quality will ooze grace and poise. He'll move with lots of energy and pick his legs up like he's in front of the judge. Even if he's just playing in the field, he'll carry his tail as high as an Arab's while dancing and prancing, and can perform an extended trot that's almost as good as Valegro's along the fenceline.

Some famous horses and ponies who have true star quality...

- Valegro (ridden by Charlotte Dujardin)
- Teddy the Shetland
- Vanir Kamira (ridden by Piggy March)
- Mickey (owned by This Esme)
- Uthopia (ridden by Carl Hester)

PONY
magazine

Be a better rider with our fantastic training features

Learn everything you need to know about pony care

Keep up to date with your fave riders and behind-the-scenes horsey action

A PONY BORED JAR

Never run out of schooling ideas with this awesome make

YOU'LL NEED

✓ Jar
✓ Lolly sticks or paper
✓ Paint or felt-tips
✓ Glue stick

CREATE A PONY QUIZ

BORED JAR

DRAW...
LEAN TACK
READ PONY
PONY COLOURIN

TOP TIP
Why not make your jar with friends, you'll have more ideas between you!

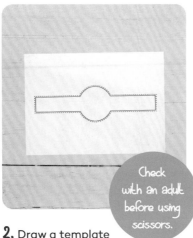

Give your jar a thorough wash and remove any labels.

2. Draw a template that will fit your jar.

Check with an adult before using scissors.

3. Decorate your label however you'd like. We used loads of colours to make it stand out.

Carefully cut out your label – try to keep it as neat as possible!

TOP TIP
You could use sticky tape instead of glue.

5. Stick the label on to your jar with a glue stick. Make it as straight as you can.

To-do examples

Exercising
- flatwork
- polework
- hacking
- jumping
- groundwork

Yard jobs
- pony pamper sesh
- spring-clean stable
- clean tack
- tidy tack room
- poo-pick

Learn about ponies
- read a pony book
- watch pro rider vids
- read PONY mag
- take a pony quiz
- book a riding lesson

Pony fun
- write a pony story
- draw a pony picture
- bake a pony treat
- create a pony quiz
- pony colouring-in

Write out your to-dos on the lolly sticks. Make sure your writing's really easy to read.

7. Pop your to-dos into the jar, muddling them up to make sure you pull them out at random.

BOREDOM CURED!

You'll always have plenty of fun things to try with your pony!

Little 'n' Large

YONAGUNI AND PERCHERONS

Have you heard about these breeds before?

DID YOU KNOW?

Yonaguni ponies are one of the eight breeds native to Japan, alongside the Miyako and Tokora horses.

Yippee for Yonaguni

Historically an essential part of Japanese rural life, Yonaguni horses are now critically endangered, with just 130 living in Japan. As technology advanced, Yonaguni horses became less important and their numbers fell – in 1975 there were just 59. Eventually, an independent association was formed that has made huge efforts to increase the population and protect the breed for the future.

Now, the breed has become an important part of Japanese tourism. The island the ponies call home is only 11 square miles and has around 2,000 residents. The horses are semi-wild, but their friendly and calm personalities mean they're usually unfazed by tourists – they seem to love lying on the island's white sand beaches!

FACT FILE

Home country: Yonaguni Island, Japan
Height: 10–12hh
Colours: Bay, brown, cremello or roan
Uses: Tourist attraction

Perfect Percherons

Clever, willing and strong, Percherons originated in the 17th Century and were bred as war horses. Eventually, they were used to pull stagecoaches, in agriculture and for hauling heavy goods. The very first Percheron stud book was formed in 1883 in France, while the British Percheron Horse Society was started around 1918.

Thousands of these horses were transported to the USA before the First World War, and the US Percheron registry was made in 1934 – today around 2,500 horses are registered every year in the USA alone! Every year since 1978, the World Percheron Congress has been held at various venues across the world, including in Britain, France and the USA.

FACT FILE

Home country: Huisne River valley, France
Height: 15.1–19hh
Colours: Grey or black (roan, bay and chestnut horses can be registered, but only in the USA)
Uses: Driving and riding

TERRIFIC TENTPEGGING

*Could this exciting sport be your new fave?
Learn more here and give it a go!*

Tentpegging's been around for almost 2,500 years! It's all about speed and precision, so it's no wonder the sport's been popular for so long and continues to be today.

PONY recommends you wear an up-to-standard riding hat when mounted at all times

Know the rules
The game's played by galloping down a line and using a sword or lance to pierce, pick up and carry a small target. It's done individually, in pairs or teams of four. A quick pace is essential, as competitors need to meet an optimum time to avoid penalties.

The rules vary and can affect...
- the size (2.5–7.5cm) and material of the target
- how many targets are on the course
- the weight and length of the lance or sword
- the minimum time for the course to be completed in

Origin story

Tentpegging's been played in Europe and Asia for a really long time, but the exact location in which it started is tough to pin down. Most people believe that tentpegging originated in India as a tactic used against elephant mounted troops.

We do know that the sport evolved from cavalry training exercises, which were designed to test riders' abilities with a sword and lance while in the saddle. It's developed into one of the most popular skill-at-arms games, which is why the whole class of sports that use a lance or sword is now known as tentpegging.

Give it a go

If you want to try tentpegging, you totally can! But it's a great idea to help get your pony used to what you'll be doing at home first. Here's how the British Tentpegging Association suggest doing it...

- practise riding one-handed, with the reins in your left hand, in all paces – start slowly, though!
- made a practice lance out of a broom handle to get your pony used to you carrying one while you ride. You can start by using a schooling whip to get him used to having it around
- have a go at leaning down the right-hand side of your pony so he gets used to your weight shifting – he should keep moving straight even if you're leaning to the side
- ride past targets on the ground so your pony doesn't spook when you're trying to catch one
- get used to keeping the tip of your lance pointing up!

SHOOTING FOR THE STARS

Leonie steps into the shoes of a pro rider

Seventeen-year old Leonie had spent the summer working as a groom at Moonline Stud – the prestigious showjumping yard where pro rider Michelle McPherson was based. It was part of her college apprenticeship and Leonie had learnt loads about horse care while working there. She'd even had the chance to improve her riding skills exercising the gorgeous showjumpers.

A close bond

Even though Leonie loved all the horses at Moonline Stud, there was one who she adored the most. Her name was Cleopatra's Treasure, Cleo for short. A stunning chestnut Holsteiner, she was one of Michelle's most promising young horses and, though Leonie had never ridden her, she was in charge of her day- to-day care. Over the months Leonie had worked at the stud, she and Cleo had formed a strong bond. It took a while for her to warm to Leonie but, over time, they reached an understanding. Cleo often chilled out while Leonie groomed her and plaited her up for competitions. Her next outing would be Orlanda Horse Show – one of the biggest comps in the country. It had always been Leonie's dream to ride there one day, but travelling as part of her horsey hero's entourage was the next best thing.

> **The plan was completely and utterly bonkers**

A strange encounter

When Team McPherson arrived at the show, Leonie and head groom Richard worked hard to settle in the horses and prepare for the days ahead. She paid special attention to Cleo, as her class had the most riding on it – the Golden League Final.

Over the first two days of the show, all of Michelle's horses performed brilliantly. One evening, Leonie was about to lock up the tack room when she bumped into Richard. "Leave it open. I'm just going to grab Comanche's bridle to wipe over." Leonie thought this was strange, but nodded anyway. But she couldn't help but linger outside the doorway a moment as she heard Richard's phone ring. "I'll get it done. She'll be yours soon, I promise," he said, in hushed tones.

Disaster strikes

That morning, Michelle had a class on Comanche. Richard was in charge of tacking him up, and Leonie watched from the sidelines. Michelle was riding well, but on the second-to-last fence Leonie watched in horror as Michelle's saddle started to slip, and she fe to the floor with a hard smack. Richard ran out to gr Comanche while Leonie ran to help Michelle to her feet. The paramedics beat her to it, but she brushed them off quickly.

Leonie helped Michelle to the lorry but it was clea her arm was really hurt. "There's no way I'll be able to ride Cleo," Michelle said when it was just the two of them. "It's okay – there'll be other shows," Leonie said reassuringly, as she passed Michelle a bottle of water. "There won't... not for Cle Michelle sounded miserable. "W not?" Leonie asked.

"Mrs Cobb, her owner... This was my last chance to prove Cl was worthy of something. If she doesn't do well in this class she' be sold, along with a lot of my other rides."

The thought of Michelle losin her horses made Leonie's heart sink. But she noticed that Mich was looking her up and down. "Unless..." she pondered. "What? asked Leonie. "Unless you ride pretending to be me."

Leonie froze, trying to process what Michelle had just said. "Me?" she gasped. "Why not? We're about the same size and both have brown hair." Michelle w thinking out loud. "From our training sessions I know you're capable. It might just save my career."

Stepping up

Hearing Michelle's encouraging words, Leonie couldn help but agree. Quickly, she was dressed in Michelle' best show gear. She looked like a real professional and it all felt like a dream. Michelle would watch a livestream of the class from the lorry so no one coul see her. Leonie stepped out and quickly tacked up Cleo, whispering in her ear to let her know the plan.

As Leonie walked Cleo towards the warm-up arena, Richard crossed in front of her. She quickly turned her head away, not trusting him. "Michelle!" h called. "You're... okay after the fall?" He sounded real

cked. Leonie quickly rode away, murmuring a short
y so he didn't have time to recognise her.

e main event

o was absolutely incredible to ride. Leonie had
er felt that kind of power in a horse before. This
ld be the highest course she'd ever jumped, but she
all her trust in Cleo.
Soon, the steward ushered them towards the ring.
they entered, the crowd cheered. "And next up we
e Michelle McPherson riding Cleopatra's Treasure,"
commentator announced. Leonie's stomach
ched. The plan was completely and utterly bonkers.
, it was too late to back out now.
Before she knew it, Leonie was cantering Cleo round
ring. The bell sounded and the crowd fell silent –
nie rode at the first fence, holding her breath as
y took off. Sure enough, they cleared it and the rest
he course passed in a blur. They soared over each
ce, including the huge water tray and triple bar.
lly, Leonie rode over the triple, pushing Cleo on to
and beat the time. Sure enough, the crowd went
d when they crossed the finish line. They'd done it!
nie gave Cleo a big hug around her sweaty neck.

inner takes all

k at the warm-up arena, Michelle was at the
gside, wearing a dark hoodie so no one would
ognise her. Leonie jumped off, but her legs instantly
nt to jelly from the adrenaline rush. The two walked

back to the lorry, talking in hushed tones.
Michelle congratulated her, then explained what
she'd discovered. While Leonie had been warming up
Cleo, she'd had gone to check over Comanche's tack to
try to understand what had gone wrong. As she stood
in the back of the lorry she'd overheard Richard talking
to a rival showjumper, Bill Broadbent. It turned out that
he was a double agent, working against Michelle to
help Bill get the ride on Cleo.
A voice came over the loudspeaker, announcing
that Cleo had come second and Michelle whooped
with delight just as Cleo's owner appeared by the lorry
ramp. But then her face fell as she realised she'd have
to confess what they'd done. Michelle ushered Mrs
Cobb to one side and explained what had happened,
and how Richard had sabotaged her round on
Comanche. The two hurried off to the show organiser's
office, while Leonie untacked Cleo and nervously
waited for news.
Soon Michelle and Mrs Cobb returned. Richard
and Bill Broadbent had been escorted from the
showground and, while Cleo had to forfeit her place
in the class, no further action would be taken against
Michelle. Mrs Cobb wanted Michelle to keep the rides
on her horses, and they were both so impressed with
Leonie's riding that she was offered a permanent
position as head groom, which included training on
all of Michelle's top horses. There was no telling where
her career would take her and, one day, maybe Leonie
would become a more famous rider than Michelle!

READY FOR MY CLOSE-UP QUIZ

Page 20

1. Shavings fork
2. Bucket
3. Sponge
4. Hoof pick
5. Salt lick
6. Girth straps
7. Stirrup
8. Leadrope
9. Tendon boot
10. Dandy brush
11. Massage mitt
12. Rug

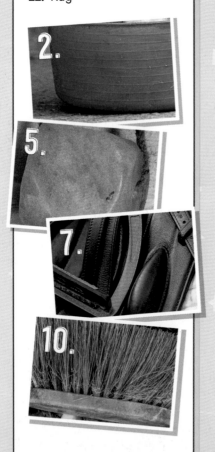

FACT OR FICTION QUIZ

Page 70

1.	False	6.	True	11.	True	16.	False
2.	True	7.	False	12.	False	17.	True
3.	False	8.	True	13.	True	18.	False
4.	False	9.	True	14.	False	19.	True
5.	False	10.	False	15.	True	20.	True

FROM HEAD TO TOE QUIZ

Page 84

1. Muzzle
2. Poll
3. Crest
4. Withers
5. Croup
6. Hock
7. Fetlock
8. Hoof
9. Pastern
10. Knee

A PONY STRING ARTWORK

Use this template for your string pony, or scan it and scale it up to make a larger one!

Page 38

YOU CAN ALSO DOWNLOAD THE TEMPLATE AT bit.ly/ANNUAL2022_ TEMPLATES

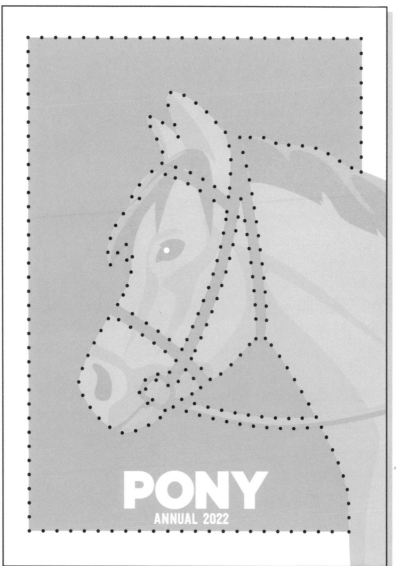

PONY
ANNUAL 2022

WHO TOOK THE PICS

Photography Bob Atkins, Lucy Merrell, n Stroud, shutterstock.com
ver photo Jon Stroud
ver insets Lucy Merrell, Jon Stroud
2–23 Ervin Monn / Shutterstock.com

p40–43 frantic00 / Shutterstock.com
p62–63 EleanorAbramson / Shutterstock.com, Christopher Halloran / Shutterstock.com
p78–79 John Aron Photography

p86–87 COLOMBO NICOLA / Shutterstock.com, Restuccia Giancarlo / Shutterstock.com
p102–103 Illustrations by Helena Öhmark and Rebecca Öhmark

THE MISADVENTURES OF CHARLIE!